G000137731

EM 23

ACTIVE MATHEMATICS 2

B. V. Hony

Oundle School

ACTIVE MATHEMATICS

Pupils' book 1   0 582 08439 3
Teacher's guide 1   0 582 08444 X

B. V. Hony

Pupils' book 2   0 582 08440 7
Teacher's guide 2   0 582 08445 8

B. V. Hony

Pupils' book 3   0 582 08441 5
Teacher's guide 3   0 582 08446 6

B. V. Hony and D. A. Turner

Pupils' book 4   0 582 08442 3
Teacher's guide 4   0 582 08447 4

D. A. Turner, B. V. Hony, I. A. Potts, K. D. Oakley and P. S. Lane

Pupils' book 5   0 582 08443 1
Teacher's guide 5   0 582 08448 2

D. A. Turner, B. V. Hony, I. A. Potts and K. D. Oakley

Longman Group UK Limited
*Longman House, Burnt Mill, Harlow, Essex CM20 2JE, England
and Associated Companies throughout the world.*

First published by Active Publications 1988
© Active Publications

Second edition first published by Longman Group UK Limited 1992
© Longman Group UK Limited 1992

*All rights reserved. No part of this publication may be
reproduced, stored in a retrieval system, or transmitted in
any form or by any means, electronic, mechanical,
photocopying, recording, or otherwise without either the
prior written permission of the Publishers or a licence
permitting restricted copying issued by the Copyright
Licensing Agency Ltd, 90 Tottenham Court Road, London W1P 9HE.*

First published 1992
ISBN 0 582 08440 7

Set in Times by Ellis Associates
Printed in Singapore
Produced by Longman Singapore Publishers Pte Ltd

TO THE USER OF THIS BOOK

You should enjoy using this book, especially if you like fast things, large things, interesting things or challenging things. You will be taught the tools of the maths trade and how to use them.

The tools of the trade

- To calculate on paper, in your head and with a calculator.
- To explain on paper what you are doing and how you are doing it.
- To use the basic skills of maths.

Using the tools of the trade

- To compare the sizes of numbers and quantities.
- To make scale drawings.
- To read scales and to use simple graphs.
- To work out speeds, area, length, volume, costs and profits.
- To use algebra to solve problems.
- To solve simple science problems.
- To investigate problems which may not have a single answer.
- To do project work.

About this book

Each chapter contains brief notes on the principles involved, followed by worked EXAMPLES of every type of problem. The REMEMBER boxes give useful hints. ACTIVITIES help to apply the principles.

The problems in the EXERCISES are graded and include some real challenges in the MASTERMINDER sections.

Learn more about the way maths can be applied in the COURSEWORK pages (marked by a grey bar down the edge of the page).

Finally, have some fun with the PUZZLERS at the end of each chapter.

CONTENTS

To the user of this book

___ Chapter 1 ARITHMETIC I

1.1 Basic principles *1*
1.2 Decimals *7*
1.3 Fractions *9*
1.4 Directed numbers *14*
1.5 The calculator *17*
1.6 Percentages *25*

Revision Exercises *27*
Basics Test 1, Puzzlers *28*
Coursework: Protein yield *29*

___ Chapter 2 ALGEBRA I

2.1 Basic principles *30*
2.2 Symbolic expression *32*
2.3 Brackets *34*
2.4 Substitution *35*
2.5 Equations *38*
2.6 Problem solving *39*
2.7 Sequences *41*

Revision Exercises *45*
Basics Test 2, Puzzler *46*
Coursework: Straight lines and circles *47*

___ Chapter 3 PROPORTION

3.1 Basic principles *48*
3.2 Change of units *52*
3.3 Exchange rates *55*
3.4 Problem solving *57*
3.5 Science problems *60*

Revision Exercises *62*
Basics Test 3, Puzzlers *63*
Coursework: The Humber Bridge *64*

___ Chapter 4 GEOMETRY I

4.1 Basic principles *65*
4.2 Parallel lines *68*
4.3 Symmetry of quadrilaterals *71*
4.4 Rotational symmetry *73*
4.5 Angles of a polygon *74*
4.6 Miscellaneous calculations *76*

Revision Exercises *78*
Basics Test 4, Puzzlers *79*
Coursework: Parallel lines *80*

Chapter 5 GRAPHS I

5.1 Basic principles *81*
5.2 Drawing graphs *82*
5.3 Using graphs *86*

Revision Exercises *90*
Basics Test 5, Puzzlers *92*
Coursework: Imperial to metric units *93*

Chapter 6 ALGEBRA II

6.1 Multiplication and division *95*
6.2 Fractions *99*
6.3 Factors *101*
6.4 Substitution *103*
6.5 Equations *104*

Revision Exercises *107*
Basics Test 6, Puzzlers *108*
Coursework: A paper-folding problem *109*

Chapter 7 ARITHMETIC II

7.1 Index form *110*
7.2 Standard form *114*
7.3 Percentages *116*
7.4 Cross-number *121*

Revision Exercises *122*
Basics Test 7, Puzzlers *123*
Coursework: Costing electricity *124*

Chapter 8 STATISTICS AND PROBABILITY

8.1 Basic principles *125*
8.2 Pie charts *128*
8.3 Probability *132*

Revision Exercises *135*
Basics Test 8, Puzzlers *136*
Coursework: Memory investigation *137*

Chapter 9 GRAPHS II

9.1 Travel graphs *138*
9.2 Information graphs *145*

Revision Exercises *147*
Aural Test 1, Puzzlers *149*
Coursework: Animal speed records *150*

Chapter 10 TRANSFORMATIONS

10.1 Basic algebraic graphs *151*
10.2 Reflections *152*
10.3 Rotations *156*
10.4 Translations *159*
10.5 Miscellaneous transformations *161*

Revision Exercises *163*
Aural Test 2, Puzzlers *164*
Coursework: The snooker-ball problem *165*

CONTENTS

Chapter 11 ALGEBRA III

11.1 Basic principles *166*
11.2 Area *169*
11.3 Graphs and area *172*
11.4 Speed *174*
11.5 Formulae *176*
11.6 Inequalities *179*

Revision Exercises *183*
Aural Test 3, Puzzlers *184*
Coursework: Active Maths Puzzle *185*

Chapter 12 GEOMETRY II

12.1 Basic principles *186*
12.2 Bearings and maps *187*
12.3 Scale drawing *192*
12.4 Angle of depression *195*

Revision Exercises *197*
Aural Test 4, Puzzler *198*
Coursework: Polyhedra constructions *199*

Appendix: Extension work *201*
Multiple Choice Tests *210*

Acknowledgements *218*

Active Mathematics and the National Curriculum

Level	4	5	6	7	8	9	10
Book 1	■	■	■				
Book 2		■	■	■			
Book 3			■	■	■		
Book 4				■	■	■	
Book 5							■

1 ARITHMETIC I

1.1 Basic principles

Problem solving

You should solve problems in three stages. First, write down in **words** what you are trying to find. Second, show all your **working**. And third, write down the **answer**.

REMEMBER

[W] Words

[W] Working

[A] Answer

■ *EXAMPLE 1*

The most pills ever swallowed by a patient is 565 900 over 21 years. How many is this per day, to the nearest whole number?

Number of days in 21 years = 21 × 365 = 7665

[W]   Number of pills swallowed per day

[W] $= \dfrac{565\,900}{7665}$

[A]   = 74   (to the nearest whole number)

Fractions

A fraction is the ratio of two numbers, for example, $\frac{4}{6}$. The fraction $\frac{4}{6}$ stands for 4 out of 6 parts, or 4 divided by 6.

This fraction chart represents $\frac{4}{6}$.

Without changing the **value** of a fraction, it can be written in a number of ways. For example, $\frac{4}{6}$ is the same as $\frac{2}{3}, \frac{12}{18}, \dots$

$\dfrac{4}{6} \xrightarrow{\div 2} \xrightarrow{\div 2} \dfrac{2}{3}$ or $\dfrac{4}{6} \xrightarrow{\times 3} \xrightarrow{\times 3} \dfrac{12}{18}$ $\dfrac{\text{Numerator}}{\text{Denominator}}$

REMEMBER

The **value** of a fraction remains unchanged if both the numerator and denominator are multiplied (or divided) by the same number.

The four rules of number – the basic 'tools of the trade' – are adding, subtracting, multiplying and dividing. To remind yourself how to apply the four rules to fractions, look carefully at the following examples.

■ *EXAMPLE 2*

Work out: **a** $\frac{2}{3} + \frac{1}{4}$ **b** $\frac{3}{5} - \frac{2}{15}$ **c** $\frac{3}{5} \times \frac{2}{9}$ **d** $\frac{3}{7} \div \frac{9}{14}$.

a   Adding

$$\frac{2}{3} + \frac{1}{4} = \frac{8}{12} + \frac{3}{12} = \frac{11}{12}$$

> **REMEMBER**
>
> To **add** and **subtract** fractions: they must have the same denominators (they must be 'like terms').

b   Subtracting

$$\frac{3}{5} - \frac{2}{15} = \frac{9}{15} - \frac{2}{15} = \frac{7}{15}$$

c   Multiplying

$$\frac{\overset{1}{\cancel{3}}}{5} \times \frac{2}{\underset{3}{\cancel{9}}} = \frac{1}{5} \times \frac{2}{3} = \frac{2}{15}$$

> **REMEMBER**
>
> To **multiply** fractions: cancel, then multiply out.

d   Dividing

$$\frac{3}{7} \div \frac{9}{14} = \frac{\overset{1}{\cancel{3}}}{\underset{1}{\cancel{7}}} \times \frac{\overset{2}{\cancel{14}}}{\underset{3}{\cancel{9}}} = \frac{2}{3}$$

> **REMEMBER**
>
> To **divide** by a fraction: turn it upside down and multiply.

___ Decimals

The **value** of a digit is determined by where it is **placed** in relation to the decimal point. The value of each of the five digits in the number 483.26 is shown below.

Place value	Hundreds	Tens	Units	Tenths	Hundredths
Digits	4	8	3	2	6
Digit value	400	80	3	$\frac{2}{10}$	$\frac{6}{100}$

To remind yourself how to apply the four rules of number to decimals, look carefully at the following examples.

■ *EXAMPLE 3*

Find: **a** $12.46 + 9.894$ **b** $105.71 - 87.109$ **c** $319.6 \div 34$ **d** 6.54×0.95.

a   Adding

$$\begin{array}{r} 12.46 \\ +\ \ 9.894 \\ \hline 22.354 \end{array}$$

> Line up the decimal points so that 'like terms' are added or subtracted.

b   Subtracting

$$\begin{array}{r} 105.71 \\ -\ 87.109 \\ \hline 18.601 \end{array}$$

c   Dividing

$319.6 \div 34$
$= 9.4$

(Line up decimal points)

$$34\overline{)319.6}$$

(34×9) $\underline{306}$
              $13\ 6$
(34×4) $\underline{13\ 6}$
              $\overline{00\ 0}$

d   Multiplying

(Note: there is a total of 4 digits after the decimal points.)

6.54×0.95
$= 6.2130$

(Note: there is also a total of 4 digits after the decimal point in the answer.)

$$
\begin{array}{r}
654 \\
\times\ \ 95 \\
\hline
\end{array}
$$

(654×5) 3270
(654×9) $\underline{5886}$
              62130

Calculator

To remind yourself how to use a calculator, look carefully at the following examples.

Each answer is rounded to the nearest 10. Rough estimates are shown in brackets ( ). Pressing the **AC** button clears the calculator.

■ *EXAMPLE 4*

Find: **a** $\frac{36.2}{0.49} + 69$ **b** $\frac{5}{9}$ of 682   **c** $\frac{36.2 + 69}{0.49}$.

a   **AC** 36.2 **÷** 0.49 **+** 69 **=** 140

(Rough estimate: $\frac{40}{0.5} + 70 = 80 + 70 = 150$)

b   **AC** 5 **÷** 9 **×** 682 **=** 380

(Rough estimate: $\frac{5}{10} \times 700 = 350$)

c   **AC** 36.2 **+** 69 **=** **÷** 0.49 **=** 210

(Remember to press the **=** button here.)

(Rough estimate: $\frac{40 + 70}{0.5} = 110 \div 0.5 = 220$)

REMEMBER

- Carry out multiplication and division before addition and subtraction.
- Always check your answer against a rough estimate.

▃▃ Percentages

To remind yourself about different types of percentage problem, look carefully at the following examples.

■ EXAMPLE 5
Change 38% to a fraction.

$$[W] \quad 38\% \text{ as a fraction}$$

$$[W] \quad = \frac{38}{100} \quad \text{(Cancel)}$$

$$[A] \quad = \frac{19}{50}$$

■ EXAMPLE 6
What is $\frac{1}{8}$ as a percentage?

$$[W] \quad \tfrac{1}{8} \text{ as a percentage}$$

$$[W] \quad = \frac{1}{8} \times 100 \quad \text{(Cancel)}$$

$$[A] \quad = 12.5\%$$

■ EXAMPLE 7

Express 30 m as a percentage of 69 m, to the nearest whole number.

$$[W] \quad 30 \text{ m as a percentage of } 69 \text{ m}$$

$$[W] \quad = \frac{30}{69} \times 100 \quad (30 \text{ m written as a fraction of } 69 \text{ m})$$

$$[A] \quad = 43\% \quad \text{(to the nearest whole number)}$$

■ EXAMPLE 8

What is 68% of 3 hours and 23 minutes, to the nearest ten minutes?

3 hours 23 minutes = 203 minutes

$$[W] \quad 68\% \text{ of } 203 \text{ minutes}$$

$$[W] \quad = \frac{68}{100} \times 203 \text{ minutes}$$

$$[A] \quad = 140 \text{ minutes (to the nearest ten minutes)}$$

$$\approx 2 \text{ hours } 20 \text{ minutes} \quad (\approx \text{ means 'approximately equal to')}$$

■ *EXAMPLE 9* ⌨

In Scotland, there are 277 mountains over 3000 feet high. Jane has climbed 180 of them. What percentage has she not climbed?

Jane has not climbed 97 mountains.

[W]   Percentage not climbed

[W] $= \dfrac{97}{277} \times 100$ (Number **not** climbed written as a fraction of the total)

[A] $\approx 35\%$

(Note that $\frac{180}{277} \times 100 \approx 65\%$)

⎯ Exercise 1

Do not use your calculator for Questions 1 to 6. You need a calculator for questions marked ⌨.

1 Copy and complete:

a $\dfrac{1}{7} = \dfrac{4}{14} = \dfrac{4}{} = \dfrac{9}{56} = \dfrac{9}{} = \dfrac{12}{}$

b $\dfrac{2}{13} = \dfrac{2}{26} = \dfrac{18}{39} = \dfrac{18}{} = \dfrac{26}{} = \dfrac{26}{234}$

c $\dfrac{45}{180} = \dfrac{45}{120} = \dfrac{9}{60} = \dfrac{9}{} = \dfrac{1}{12} = \dfrac{1}{}$

2 Work out:

a $\dfrac{2}{3} + \dfrac{1}{6}$ **b** $\dfrac{4}{5} + \dfrac{1}{10}$ **c** $\dfrac{2}{3} - \dfrac{2}{9}$ **d** $\dfrac{5}{6} - \dfrac{5}{18}$

e $\dfrac{4}{5} \times \dfrac{15}{16}$ **f** $\dfrac{2}{13} \times \dfrac{26}{29}$ **g** $\dfrac{2}{9} \div \dfrac{1}{3}$ **h** $\dfrac{6}{11} \div \dfrac{3}{22}$

3 Work out:

a $\dfrac{1}{3} + \dfrac{1}{4}$ **b** $\dfrac{2}{5} + \dfrac{1}{2}$ **c** $1 - \dfrac{12}{13}$ **d** $\dfrac{5}{6} - \dfrac{2}{15}$

e $\dfrac{13}{14} \times \dfrac{7}{26}$ **f** $\dfrac{11}{12} \times \dfrac{18}{55}$ **g** $\dfrac{17}{20} \div \dfrac{34}{35}$ **h** $\dfrac{7}{13} \div \dfrac{9}{14}$

4 Work out:

a $36.9 + 9.6 - 12.06$ **b** $108.7 + 45.08 - 38.9$ **c** 96.2×13
d 20.4×9.7 **e** $56.16 \div 8$ **f** $57.33 \div 9$
g 13.2×0.82 **h** 0.32×0.27 **i** $78.91 \div 13$
j $15.81 \div 17$

5 Work out:

a $19.16 - 3.98 + 12.78$ **b** $614.1 - 67.08 + 23.85$ **c** 4.07×7.04
d 0.92×403 **e** $1.275 \div 15$ **f** $9.1 \div 14$
g 0.9×0.82 **h** 0.7×0.36 **i** $22.78 \div 34$
j $14.07 \div 42$

6 Change each percentage to a fraction in its lowest term.
a 78% **b** 34% **c** 24% **d** 36% **e** 96% **f** 2%

For Questions 7 to 18, check your answer with a rough estimate.

7 Work out to the nearest whole number:

a $\frac{47.9}{92} + 14.8$ **b** $\frac{87}{0.86} - 14.9$ **c** $\frac{3}{8}$ of 19.876

d $\frac{4}{7.8} \div 0.08$ **e** $\frac{6.8 + 9.7}{0.23}$ **f** $\frac{128 - 3.87}{0.708}$

8 Change to the nearest whole percentage:

a $\frac{1}{7}$ **b** $\frac{4}{9}$ **c** $\frac{28}{31}$ **d** $\frac{54}{82}$ **e** $\frac{65}{68}$ **f** $\frac{17}{39}$

9 Write the first quantity as a percentage of the second, to the nearest whole number.

a 4 cm, 7 cm   **b** 9 min, 14 min   **c** 68 kg, 98 kg

d 4.8 mm, 10.9 mm   **e** 1.9 m², 16.8 m²   **f** 270 m, 2.8 km

10 Work out, to the nearest whole number:

a 38% of 48 kg   **b** 19% of 40 km   **c** 58% of 83 cm

d 89% of 12 m²   **e** 3% of 456 g   **f** 7.4% of 73 m³

11 Which is less: $\frac{2}{7}$ of 4 km or 38% of 2.9 km?

12 An average of about 800 people are killed annually in Sri Lanka by snakes. About how many people is this each week?

13 The world tree-climbing record is 100 feet (30.4 m) in 24.8 s. How many metres (to the nearest tenth of a metre) is this per second?

14 To break the world domino-falling record, 1.5 million dominoes were set out. 1 382 101 fell down. What percentage (to the nearest whole number) did **not** fall down?

15 About five twelfths of the Earth's land surface is covered with forest. What percentage (to the nearest whole number) is **not** covered with forest?

16 The most expensive fruit ever to be sold was a punnet of raspberries. This punnet of 30 raspberries was bought at an auction in Ireland for £530. What was the average cost of each raspberry (to the nearest pound)?

17 British Telecom take about 700 million calls a day. How many calls (to the nearest whole number) is this per second?

18 The most economic fuel consumption obtained by a car was achieved at Silverstone, when a car travelled 1666.34 miles using 0.26 gallons of petrol. What was the mpg (miles per gallon) to the nearest 100?

▬ 1.2 Decimals

▬ Decimals to fractions

■ *EXAMPLE 1*

Change to a fraction in its simplest form: **a** 0.84   **b** 0.0405.

a   0.84 means $\dfrac{8}{10} + \dfrac{4}{100}$ (Change to 'like terms')

$= \dfrac{80}{100} + \dfrac{4}{100}$

$= \dfrac{84}{100} = \dfrac{21}{25}$ (Cancel)

b   0.0405 means $\dfrac{4}{100} + \dfrac{5}{10\,000}$ (Change to 'like terms')

$= \dfrac{400}{10\,000} + \dfrac{5}{10\,000}$

$= \dfrac{405}{10\,000} = \dfrac{81}{2000}$ (Cancel)

┌─ *REMEMBER*

To change a decimal into a fraction: first change each digit
after the decimal point into a fraction.

▬ Fractions to decimals

■ *EXAMPLE 2*

Change into decimals: **a** $\frac{7}{4}$ **b** $\frac{3}{8}$.

a $\frac{7}{4}$ means $7 \div 4$

$= 1.75$

$\begin{array}{r} 1.75 \\ \hline 4\,|\,7.00 \end{array}$

b $\frac{3}{8}$ means $3 \div 8$

$= 0.375$

$\begin{array}{r} 0.375 \\ \hline 8\,|\,3.000 \end{array}$

> ┌── *REMEMBER*
>
> To change a fraction into a decimal: divide the denominator
> into the numerator.

── Recurring decimals

Sometimes fractions produce a 'recurring decimal', which is shown by putting a dot over the
recurring digit(s), like this: $0.\dot{6}$, $0.\dot{3}\dot{5}$.

■ *EXAMPLE 3*

Change into decimals: **a** $\frac{1}{3}$ **b** $\frac{7}{11}$.

a $\frac{1}{3}$ $= 1 \div 3$

$\phantom{\frac{1}{3}} = 0.\dot{3}$ (Note the dot over the 3)

$$\begin{array}{r} .33333... \\ 3\overline{\smash)1.00000} \end{array}$$

b $\frac{7}{11}$ $= 7 \div 11$

$\phantom{\frac{7}{11}} = 0.\dot{6}\dot{3}$ (Note the dots over the 6 and the 3)

$$\begin{array}{r} .6363... \\ 11\overline{\smash)7.0000} \end{array}$$

── Exercise 2

Change to a fraction in its simplest form:

1 0.9	**2** 0.3	**3** 0.8	**4** 0.2	**5** 0.45
6 0.65	**7** 0.25	**8** 0.18	**9** 0.62	**10** 0.54
11 0.12	**12** 0.64	**13** 0.225	**14** 0.825	**15** 0.025
16 0.875	**17** 0.008	**18** 0.0075		

Change to a decimal:

19 $\frac{3}{5}$	**20** $\frac{3}{4}$	**21** $\frac{1}{8}$	**22** $\frac{5}{8}$	**23** $\frac{1}{50}$
24 $\frac{7}{50}$	**25** $\frac{13}{50}$	**26** $\frac{6}{25}$	**27** $\frac{9}{25}$	**28** $\frac{23}{25}$
29 $\frac{7}{40}$	**30** $\frac{3}{40}$	**31** $\frac{5}{16}$	**32** $\frac{9}{16}$	**33** $\frac{15}{16}$

Change to a recurring decimal:

34 $\frac{2}{3}$	**35** $\frac{4}{9}$	**36** $\frac{1}{6}$	**37** $\frac{2}{15}$	**38** $\frac{7}{15}$
39 $\frac{1}{15}$	**40** $\frac{5}{18}$	**41** $\frac{17}{18}$	**42** $\frac{7}{12}$	**43** $\frac{11}{12}$
44 $\frac{1}{12}$	**45** $\frac{11}{24}$	**46** $\frac{5}{11}$	**47** $\frac{8}{11}$	**48** $\frac{1}{11}$

__ 1.3 Fractions

__ Mixed numbers and improper fractions

A whole number and a fraction, such as $3\frac{3}{5}$, is called a 'mixed number'. When this number is changed to fifths ($\frac{18}{5}$), it is called an 'improper fraction'. Look carefully at the following examples.

■ *EXAMPLE 1*

a Write $3\frac{3}{5}$ as an improper fraction.   **b** Write $\frac{17}{9}$ as a mixed number.

a $3\frac{3}{5} = 3 + \frac{3}{5}$ (Change to 'like terms')

$\qquad = \frac{15}{5} + \frac{3}{5}$

$\qquad = \frac{18}{5}$

b $\frac{17}{9} = \frac{9}{9} + \frac{8}{9}$

$\qquad = 1 + \frac{8}{9} = 1\frac{8}{9}$

__ Exercise 3

Write as mixed numbers:

1 $\frac{5}{4}$ 　　　　 **2** $\frac{7}{5}$ 　　　　 **3** $\frac{13}{6}$ 　　　　 **4** $\frac{11}{3}$

5 $\frac{43}{8}$ 　　　　 **6** $\frac{22}{15}$ 　　　　 **7** $\frac{28}{10}$ 　　　　 **8** $\frac{39}{9}$

9 $\frac{60}{32}$ 　　　　 **10** $\frac{66}{24}$ 　　　　 **11** $\frac{204}{36}$ 　　　　 **12** $\frac{333}{54}$

13 $\frac{165}{30}$

Write as improper fractions:

14 $1\frac{1}{2}$ 　　　　 **15** $1\frac{5}{6}$ 　　　　 **16** $2\frac{5}{8}$ 　　　　 **17** $4\frac{3}{4}$

18 $7\frac{1}{6}$ 　　　　 **19** $3\frac{7}{20}$ 　　　　 **20** $2\frac{13}{25}$

▬ Addition and subtraction

To understand how to add and subtract mixed numbers, look carefully at the following examples.

> ┌── *REMEMBER*
>
> To add or subtract fractions: they must have the same denominators
> (they must be 'like terms').

■ *EXAMPLE 2*

Work out: **a** $3\frac{3}{5} + 2\frac{3}{4}$ **b** $6\frac{2}{3} - 2\frac{1}{6}$.

a $3\frac{3}{5} + 2\frac{3}{4} = 3 + 2 + \frac{3}{5} + \frac{3}{4}$ (Collect up like terms)

$$= 5 + \frac{12}{20} + \frac{15}{20}$$ (Change fractions to like terms)

$$= 5 + \frac{27}{20}$$ (Change fraction to a mixed number)

$$= 5 + 1 + \frac{7}{20} = 6\frac{7}{20}$$

b $6\frac{2}{3} - 2\frac{1}{6} = 6 - 2 + \frac{2}{3} - \frac{1}{6}$ (Change fractions to like terms)

$$= 4 \quad + \frac{4}{6} - \frac{1}{6}$$

$$= 4\frac{3}{6}$$ (Cancel fraction)

$$= 4\frac{1}{2}$$

▬ Exercise 4

1 $4\frac{1}{2} + 3\frac{1}{6}$ 2 $5\frac{3}{8} + 4\frac{1}{4}$ 3 $7\frac{2}{3} - 1\frac{1}{6}$ 4 $4\frac{7}{9} - 3\frac{1}{3}$

5 $6\frac{2}{5} + 7\frac{1}{3}$ 6 $8\frac{2}{11} + 2\frac{1}{2}$ 7 $4 - 2\frac{3}{8}$ 8 $7 - 5\frac{2}{5}$

9 $2\frac{3}{4} + 1\frac{1}{6}$ 10 $3\frac{5}{6} + 2\frac{1}{9}$ 11 $1\frac{3}{8} - \frac{1}{3}$ 12 $2\frac{6}{7} - \frac{1}{4}$

13 $3\frac{9}{10} + 2\frac{2}{15}$ 14 $3\frac{5}{14} + 1\frac{16}{21}$ 15 $6\frac{5}{8} - 5\frac{1}{6}$ 16 $3\frac{5}{9} - 2\frac{1}{6}$

17 $8\frac{5}{6} + 4\frac{7}{8}$ 18 $3\frac{13}{14} + 1\frac{20}{21}$

MASTERMINDERS

Solve for x in the following equations:

19 $x + 4\frac{3}{4} = 8\frac{3}{8}$

20 $1\frac{1}{5} + \frac{5}{12} = x + \frac{11}{30}$

21 $-3\frac{3}{7} = x + 5\frac{1}{6}$

22 $\frac{1}{5} - x = 2\frac{7}{10} - 3\frac{5}{6}$

23 $6\frac{3}{7} - x = 7\frac{7}{8}$

24 $\frac{3}{10} - 1\frac{19}{30} = x - 2\frac{2}{3}$

▬ Multiplication and division

The method used to multiply and divide mixed numbers is the same as the one used with simple fractions, except that all mixed numbers must first be changed to improper fractions. Look carefully at the following examples.

■ EXAMPLE 3

Work out: **a** $3\frac{2}{3} \times 4\frac{1}{2}$ **b** $5\frac{1}{3} \div 2\frac{2}{5}$.

a $3\frac{2}{3} \times 4\frac{1}{2}$ (Change to improper fractions)

$= \frac{11}{\cancel{3}_1} \times \frac{\cancel{9}^3}{2}$ (Cancel)

$= \frac{33}{2}$ (Change to a mixed number)

$= 16\frac{1}{2}$

b $5\frac{1}{3} \div 2\frac{2}{5}$ (Change to improper fractions)

$= \frac{16}{3} \div \frac{12}{5}$ (Turn $\frac{12}{5}$ upside down and multiply)

$= \frac{\cancel{16}^4}{3} \times \frac{5}{\cancel{12}_3}$ (Cancel)

$= \frac{20}{9}$ (Change to a mixed number)

$= 2\frac{2}{9}$

> *REMEMBER*
>
> To multiply and divide fractions: use only **improper** fractions.

___ Exercise 5

1 $\frac{3}{8} \times 5\frac{1}{3}$ **2** $\frac{5}{9} \times 3\frac{3}{5}$ **3** $4\frac{1}{2} \div \frac{3}{4}$ **4** $2\frac{2}{3} \div \frac{2}{9}$

5 $3\frac{1}{7} \times \frac{7}{15}$ **6** $3\frac{1}{3} \times 2\frac{5}{8}$ **7** $2\frac{1}{3} \div 2\frac{4}{5}$ **8** $1\frac{7}{8} \div 2\frac{1}{2}$

9 $2\frac{1}{2} \times 4\frac{2}{3}$ **10** $2\frac{1}{3} \times 3\frac{3}{5}$ **11** $2\frac{4}{5} \div 1\frac{3}{5}$ **12** $1\frac{3}{5} \div 2\frac{4}{5}$

13 $4 \times 2\frac{2}{3}$ **14** $2\frac{2}{3} \times 2\frac{2}{3}$ **15** $\frac{4}{2\frac{2}{3}}$ **16** $\frac{2\frac{2}{3}}{4}$

17 $5\frac{1}{3} \div 4\frac{12}{13}$ **18** $4\frac{12}{13} \div 5\frac{1}{3}$

Can you find a connection between the answers to Questions 11 and 12; 15 and 16; 17 and 18?

MASTERMINDERS

19 Simplify:

a $1 + \cfrac{1}{1 + \cfrac{1}{1+1}}$

b $1 + \cfrac{1}{1 + \cfrac{1}{1+\frac{1}{1+1}}}$

Solve for x in the following equations:

20 $2\frac{2}{3}x = 2\frac{1}{4}$ **21** $\frac{12}{25} \times \frac{7}{9} = 5x$

22 $2\frac{1}{4} = x \div 2\frac{2}{3}$ **23** $\frac{8}{15} \div \frac{2}{9} = x \div 1\frac{7}{25}$

24 $2\frac{2}{3} \div x = 2\frac{1}{4}$ **25** $\frac{3}{16} \div 1\frac{3}{7} = \frac{1}{2} \div x$

___ Problem solving

> *REMEMBER*
>
> [W]   Words
> [W]   Working
> [A]   Answer

___ Exercise 6

1 There are 180 pupils in the third year at Orchard School. They choose their sports options as follows: $\frac{1}{3}$ choose rugby, $\frac{5}{12}$ choose football, $\frac{3}{20}$ choose hockey and the rest choose cross country. Find **a** the fraction who choose cross country **b** the number who choose each of the four options.

2 A cabinet in a school library is used for storing books on nine different subjects. Copy and complete the following table.

Shelf number	Subject	No. of books	Fractional no. of books	Total no. of books on shelf
1	Maths Physics Chemistry		3/10 9/20	40
2	Woodwork Needlework Cookery	16	1/6	30
3	English French German	9	7/12 4/15	

3 A shopkeeper has a wholesale pack of sultanas, which contains $12\frac{1}{2}$ kg. She repacks the sultanas into smaller packets, each of which contains $\frac{5}{6}$ kg. How many packets does she fill?

4 **a** A lorry arrives at a depot with $13\frac{1}{2}$ tonnes of coal. The depot manager repacks the coal into bags which each contain $\frac{3}{40}$ tonnes of coal when full. How many bags does he fill?

b During the course of a year, the depot delivers 8100 tonnes of coal to customers. How many of the above lorry loads does the depot receive in one year?

5 Library A has $3\frac{1}{3}$ times as many books as Library B. If Library A has 9000 books, how many books are there in Library B?

6 Mr X and Mrs Y both have salaries of £25 000. What will be the difference in their salaries if Mr X's salary increases $2\frac{1}{2}$ times and Mrs Y's increases $2\frac{3}{4}$ times?

MASTERMINDERS

7 James and Mark get paid for gathering some rose-hips. James gathers $3\frac{1}{2}$ kg and Mark gathers $2\frac{1}{4}$ kg. If James receives 60p more than Mark, how much are they paid for gathering one kilogram?

8 In class 2A, one half of the pupils are girls and in class 2B three fifths of the pupils are girls. If both classes are sitting in the assembly hall, what fraction of the pupils are girls, if there are twice as many pupils in class 2A?

9 Jenny and Clare take chocolate bars on a picnic and agree to share them equally. Jenny brings four and Clare brings one. To square matters, Clare gives Jenny 78p. What was the price of a chocolate bar?

___ 1.4 Directed numbers

REMEMBER

Directed numbers have a plus or minus sign in them, such as (-3) and $(+8)$.

___ Addition and subtraction

If John has £5 in his savings account and withdraws £8, the bank must lend him £3. He is overdrawn by £3 and this is written −£3. Therefore:

£5 − £8 = −£3

We could say that John subtracts £8 from £5. This can be illustrated on a number line:

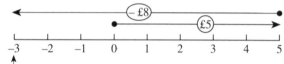

−£3 is the result of substracting £8 from £5.

If Susan has overdrawn her account by £8 and pays in £5, her balance would then be −£3. Therefore:

−£8 + £5 = −£3

We could say that Susan adds £5 to −£8. This can be illustrated on a number line:

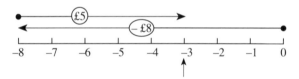

−£3 is the sum of −£8 and + £5.

___ Exercise 7

For questions 1 to 20, find:

1 £4 − £9	**2** £15 − £35	**3** 12 − 21	**4** 96 − 120
5 35 − 50 + 18	**6** £95 − £140 + £60	**7** −£5 + £9	**8** −$8 + $17
9 −8 + 3 + 7	**10** −7 + 2 + 3	**11** −$21 − $54	**12** −36 − 27
13 21 − 56 − 45	**14** −12 + 8 − 16	**15** −30 + 21 − 27	**16** −24 − 51 + 15
17 $-11\frac{1}{2} - 20\frac{1}{2}$	**18** −24.5 + 12.5 − 30	**19** −3.5 − 32.5	**20** $-40\frac{1}{4} - 26\frac{1}{4} + 21\frac{1}{2}$

21 Add 13 to minus 17.

22 Add minus 4 to minus 7.

23 Subtract 6 from minus 8.

24 Subtract 15 from minus 11.

25 Add minus 23 to 16.

26 Subtract 56.9 from minus 28.

27 Subtract minus $18\frac{1}{3}$ from $12\frac{3}{4}$.

28 What is the sum of minus 17, 28 and minus 26?

Bill says, 'Kate is not lying'. He could have said, 'Kate is not, not telling the truth'. Or he could have simply said, 'Kate is telling the truth'.

This example shows how two negatives can be replaced by a positive. It may help you to subtract with negative numbers.

■ *EXAMPLE 1*

a   Subtract (-4) from 6.
b   Add (-6) to (-3).
c   Subtract (-5) from (-8).
d   Evaluate $5 - (-7)$.
e   Evaluate $(-8) + (-10)$.

a $6 - (-4) = 6 + 4 = 10$
b $-3 + (-6) = -3 - 6 = -9$
c $-8 - (-5) = -8 + 5 = -3$
d $5 - (-7) = 5 + 7 = 12$
e $(-8) + (-10) = -8 - 10 = -18$

—— Exercise 8

For Questions 1 to 20, find:

1 $10 - (-3)$ **2** $4 - (-7)$ **3** $3 + (-1)$
4 £7 + (-£2) **5** $\$14 - (-\$42)$ **6** $\$42 - (-\$14)$
7 $18 - (+9)$ **8** $7 - (+25)$ **9** $-4 - (-7)$
10 $-23 - (-2)$ **11** $-31 - (+5)$ **12** $-8 - (+12)$
13 −£24 + (−£28) **14** −£29 −(−£17) **15** $-4\frac{3}{4} - (-2\frac{1}{2})$
16 $7\frac{2}{3} - (+3\frac{2}{3})$ **17** $2\frac{2}{3} + (-8\frac{1}{3})$ **18** $-4.5 - (+7.5)$
19 $-2.3 - (+3.2)$ **20** $-19.4 - (-19.4)$

21 Add (-7) to (-8). **22** Subtract (-12) from (-17).

23 Subtract (-26) from (-19). **24** Add (-6) to (-6) to (-6).

25 Subtract £76 from £67.

MASTERMINDERS

26 Subtract $\$25.5$ from $(-\$34.5)$.

27 Add (-12) to 45 and subtract the result from (-28).

28 Subtract (-4) from (-4) and subtract the result from (-4).

___ Multiplication and division

The number line to illustrate $-2 - 2 - 2$
is shown here.

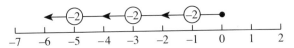

$$-2 - 2 - 2 \;=\; 3 \times (-2)$$
$$= -(3 \times 2) = -6$$

The same product $(-(3 \times 2))$ can be
considered in another way, like this:

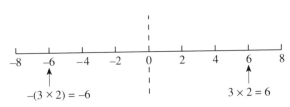

The negative sign can therefore be regarded as an indicator which shows a 'reflection' in the
'mirror line' through zero.

Now consider the product $(-3) \times (-2)$.

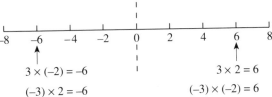

As there are **two** negative signs in the product, there must be **two** reflections in the line
through zero.

Therefore $(-3) \times (-2) = +6$.

> _REMEMBER_
>
> When multiplying directed numbers:
> - **Like** signs give a **positive** result: $(-3) \times (-2) = +6$
> - **Unlike** signs give a **negative** result: $(-3) \times (+2) = -6$

The same two rules are also true for dividing directed numbers.

∎EXAMPLE 2

Work out the following:

a $4 \times (-1)$ **b** $(-2) \times (-12)$ **c** $(-16) \div 2$ **d** $\frac{-60}{-15}$ **e** $(-3) \times (-8) \div (-6)$.

a $4 \times (-1) = -4$

b $(-2) \times (-12) = 24$

c $(-16) \div 2 = -8$

d $\dfrac{-60}{-15} = \dfrac{-4}{-1} = 4$

e $(-3) \times (-8) \div (-6) = 24 \div (-6) = -4$

___ Exercise 9

For Questions 1 to 20, find:

1 $3 \times (-12)$
2 $15 \times (-6)$
3 $(-21) \times 5$
4 $(-16) \times (-2)$
5 $(-18) \times (-6)$
6 $(-96) \div 8$
7 $(-112) \div 7$
8 $144 \div (-6)$
9 $(-91) \div (-7)$
10 $(-225) \div (-75)$
11 $(-6) \times 8 \times 5$
12 $(-15) \times 7 \times 2$
13 $9 \times (-7) \times 4$
14 $12 \times 5 \times (-3)$
15 $\frac{25}{-5}$
16 $\frac{-63}{9}$
17 $\frac{-108}{-12}$
18 $\frac{-169}{-1.3}$
19 $315 \div (-15) \times (-12)$
20 $(-450) \div (-18) \times (-8)$

21 Multiply (-13) by 4.
22 Divide (-6) by (-2).
23 Multiply (-3) by (-4).

24 Find the sum of $(-7) \times (-5)$ and (-4).

25 What is the difference between (-27) and $(-3)^3$?

MASTERMINDERS

26 How many times will (-15) divide into the sum of (-25) and (-200)?

27 Subtract $(-2)^2$ from $(-2)^3$.

28 Divide (-0.1) by 1000.

___ 1.5 The calculator

When you use your calculator to work out how many times 17 will divide into 45, the following answer will be displayed:

2.647 058 8

The last digit has a value of $\frac{8}{10\,000\,000}$. Clearly, for the majority of calculations this amount of accuracy is unnecessary.

> ___ *REMEMBER*
>
> Answers can be written to the nearest 100, the nearest 10, the nearest whole number, etc.
> - 2.647 058 8 is 3 to the nearest whole number
> - 2.647 058 8 is 2.6 to the nearest tenth
> - 2.647 058 8 is 2.65 to the nearest hundredth

A more convenient way of indicating the amount of accuracy is to use either decimal places (DP) or significant figures (SF).

___ Decimal places (DP)

In Example 1 **a**, the digit 5 in 30.586 is in the 'first decimal place' (1 DP) in the number.
In Example 1 **b**, the digit 0 immediately after the decimal point in 0.049 07 is in the 'first decimal place' in the number. Look carefully at the Example.

■ *EXAMPLE 1*

Number	Number written to		
	1 DP	*2 DP*	*3 DP*
a 30.586	30.6	30.59	30.586
b 0.04907	0.0	0.05	0.049

___ Exercise 10

1 To how many decimal places (DP) are the following numbers written:
12.5,   23.87,   100.456,   0.08,   0.0809,   1.870,   7.700,   0.090 90?

2 Correct each of the following to 1 DP:
    a 1.68   **b** 5.71   **c** 0.37   **d** 0.92   **e** 3.456
    f 4.087   **g** 2.08   **h** 4.03   **i** 0.0048

3 Correct each of the following to 2 DP:
    a 3.249   **b** 1.627   **c** 4.581   **d** 0.153   **e** 3.425
    f 2.4724   **g** 5.7381   **h** 1.3602   **i** 0.5946

4 Correct each of the following to 3 DP:
    a 2.5364   **b** 8.1487   **c** 0.3942   **d** 3.827 34   **e** 1.452 93
    f 4.613 56   **g** 2.970 02   **h** 0.7399   **i** 0.003 49

___ Significant figures (SF)

In Example 2 **a**, the digit 3 in 30.586 is called the 'first significant figure' in the number.
In Example 2 **b**, the digit 4 in 0.049 07 is the 'first significant figure'. Look carefully at the Example.

■ *EXAMPLE 2*

Number	Number written to		
	1 SF	*2 SF*	*3 SF*
a 30.586	30	31	30.6
b 0.04907	0.05	0.049	0.0491

___ Exercise 11

1   To how many significant figures are the following numbers written:
431,   430,   431.4,   431.40,   0.25,   0.250,   0.025,   6800,   50.04,   0.004
0.040 302 0?

2   Correct each of the following to 1 SF:
   a 4.8   **b** 3.25   **c** 0.74   **d** 0.361   **e** 91
   f 752   **g** 870   **h** 0.034   **i** 0.0057

3   Correct each of the following to 2 SF:
   a 5.32   **b** 4.15   **c** 6.97   **d** 64.7   **e** 38.1
   f 954   **g** 698   **h** 7230   **i** 0.856

4   Correct each of the following to 3 SF:
   a 6.217   **b** 2.942   **c** 1.629   **d** 34.56   **e** 951.8
   f 476.3   **g** 6871   **h** 0.8136   **i** 0.056 27

___ Mixed operations

___ *Activity 1* ▦

1   Use your calculator to work out:
   a $6 + 5 - 4$ **b** $6 - 4 + 5$ **c** $6 \div 4 \times 2$ **d** $6 \times 2 \div 4$
   e $30 - 6 \div 3$ **f** $30 \div 3 - 6$ **g** $20 \times 2 + 4$ **h** $20 + 4 \times 2$
   Comment on your answers. Try to explain why the answer to part **e** is not 8, and the answer to part **h** is not 48.

2   If we want an addition or a subtraction to be done before either a multiplication or division, we must use **brackets**. Your calculator should have these buttons:

   (opens brackets   ) closes brackets

   Now carry out the following two sets of calculator instructions and comment on your answers:

   a (30 — 6) ÷ 3 =

   b (20 + 4) × 2 =

3   Your calculator should also have two other buttons:

   x^2 squares a number $\sqrt{}$ square roots a number

   Now carry out the following sets of calculator instructions and comment on your answers:

   a 2 × 4 x^2 =

   b (2 × 4) x^2

   c Display any number, press x^2, then press $\sqrt{}$.

You should have concluded from this Activity that some operations must be done before others. The following will help you remember the order of priority.

NOTE

Brackets	**B**
Indices	**I**
Division	**D**
Multiplication	**M**
Addition	**A**
Subtraction	**S**

The ^{2} of 5^2 is called the **index** (plural indices). An index can be $+$ or $-$, and any size from very small to very large.

▬ **Approximations**

To work out an approximate answer to a calculation, we first correct each number to one significant figure. Look carefully at the following examples.

■ EXAMPLE 3

Find the approximate answer to:

a $\dfrac{683 + 48.7}{32.9}$ **b** $\dfrac{38^2 - 394}{0.384}$ **c** $(38.6 + 15.9)^2$ **d** $\sqrt{110} \times \dfrac{56.9}{0.37}$

a $\dfrac{683 + 48.7}{32.9} \approx \dfrac{700 + 50}{30} = \dfrac{750}{30} = 25$

b $\dfrac{38^2 - 394}{0.384} \approx \dfrac{40^2 - 400}{0.4} = \dfrac{1200}{0.4} = 3000$

c $(38.6 + 15.9)^2 \approx (40 + 20)^2 = 3600$

d $\sqrt{110} \times \dfrac{56.9}{0.37} \approx 10 \times \dfrac{60}{0.4} = 1500$

NOTE

When dividing a number by a number less than 1, first multiply both numbers by a multiple of 10.

For example, $\dfrac{300}{0.6} = \dfrac{300 \times 10}{0.6 \times 10} = \dfrac{3000}{6} = 500$

— Calculations

— *Activity 2* ▦

In this Activity, we are going to explore different ways of writing a question with the numbers 9.8, 4 and 7.

1 Write down the calculation given by the calculator instructions shown below and also write down the answer. Comment on your results.

a 9.8 **+** 4 **×** 7 **=**

b 4 **×** 7 **+** 9.8 **=**

c **(** 9.8 **+** 4 **)** **×** 7 **=**

2 Work out the following with your calculator and give each answer correct to 3 SF:

a $9.8 - 4 \div 7$ **b** $9.8 \div (4 - 7)$ **c** $9.8 \div (4 + 7)$
d $(9.8 - 4) \div 7$ **e** $(9.8 + 4) \div 7$ **f** $9.8 + 4 \div 7$

Use your answers to parts **a** to **f** to write down the answers to parts **g** to **l**. (Do not use your calculator.)

g $\dfrac{9.8 - 4}{7}$ **h** $\dfrac{9.8 + 4}{7}$ **i** $9.8 + \dfrac{4}{7}$

j $9.8 - \dfrac{4}{7}$ **k** $\dfrac{9.8}{4 + 7}$ **l** $\dfrac{9.8}{4 - 7}$

3 Use your calculator to work out the exact answer to the following:

a $9.8 \times 4 \div 7$ **b** $9.8 \times (4 \div 7)$ **c** $(9.8 \times 4) \div 7$
d $9.8 \div 4 \times 7$ **e** $9.8 \div (4 \times 7)$ **f** $(9.8 \div 4) \times 7$

Explain why some of your answers are the same.

So far you should have worked out the answer to eleven different questions which have been written with the numbers 9.8, 4 and 7 in that order. In part 4 we explore eleven other ways.

4 Without using your calculator, copy and complete the following by inserting the correct sign in the ☐.

a $9.8 \; \square \; 4 \; \square \; 7 = 274.4$ **b** $9.8 \; \square \; 4 \; \square \; 7 = 20.8$

c $9.8 \; \square \; 4 \; \square \; 7 = 6.8$ **d** $9.8 \; \square \; 4 \; \square \; 7 = 9.45$

e $9.8 \; \square \; 4 \; \square \; 7 = -1.2$ **f** $9.8 \; \square \; 4 \; \square \; 7 = 32.2$

g $9.8 \; \square \; 4 \; \square \; 7 = 12.8$ **h** $9.8 \; \square \; 4 \; \square \; 7 = -18.2$

i $9.8 \; \square \; 4 \; \square \; 7 = -4.55$ **j** $(9.8 \; \square \; 4) \; \square \; 7 = 40.6$

k $9.8 \; \square \; (4 \; \square \; 7) = -29.4$

Use your calculator to check your answers.

■ *EXAMPLE 4* ▦

Work out each of the following to 3 SF. Give an approximation for each in brackets after the answer.

a $\dfrac{7.4^2}{6.9 \times 1.2}$ **b** $\sqrt{\dfrac{78}{9.84}}$

a   The calculator operations are:

[AC] 7.4 [x^2] [÷] [( ] 6.9 [×] 1.2 [ )] [=] 6.61 to 3 SF   (Approximation: $\frac{50}{7} \approx 7$)

b   The calculator operations are:

[AC] 78 [÷] 9.84 [=] [√] 2.82 to 3 SF   (Approximation: $\sqrt{\frac{80}{10}} = \sqrt{8} \approx 3$)

REMEMBER

- Do not write down the calculator operations.
- It should **not** be necessary to write down all eight digits from the calculator before writing down the corrected answer.
- Give an approximate answer in brackets.

___ Exercise 12

1 ▦ Find, correct to 2 SF, and give an approximate answer in brackets:

   a $29.4 \div (3.9 + 10.4)$ **b** $\dfrac{29.4}{3.9 + 10.4}$ **c** $3.9 - \dfrac{10.4}{29.4}$ **d** $\dfrac{29.4}{10.4} - 3.9$

2 ▦ Find, correct to 2 DP, and give an approximate answer in brackets:

   a $68.3 \times \sqrt{2.8}$ **b** $\dfrac{2.8^2}{68.3}$ **c** $\dfrac{2.8}{\sqrt{68.2}}$ **d** $\sqrt{2.8} - 68.3$

3 ▦ Find, correct to 3 SF, and give an approximate answer in brackets:

   a $\dfrac{204 - 7.08}{62.8}$ **b** $204 \times \dfrac{7.08}{62.8}$ **c** $\dfrac{204}{62.8 - 7.08}$ **d** $\dfrac{204}{62.8} - 7.08$

4 ▦ Find, to 3 DP, and give an approximate answer in brackets:

   a 4.3×0.54^2 **b** $(4.3 \times 0.54)^2$ **c** $\left(\dfrac{0.54}{4.3}\right)^2$ **d** $\sqrt{\dfrac{0.54}{4.3}}$

5 Write down two different sets of calculator operations to work out:

$$\frac{69}{12 \times 7.6}$$

   Use both methods to work out the answer, correct to 2 DP.

6 Find the mistakes in the calculator operations shown below:

a $4 \div 2 + 6$ **b** $6 + \frac{7}{9}$ **c** $\frac{3}{4+9}$ **d** $\frac{4}{7 \times 3}$

a `AC` 4 `÷` 2 `+` 6

b `AC` 6 `(` 7 `÷` 9 `)` `=`

c `AC` 3 `÷` 4 `+` 9 `=`

d `AC` 4 `÷` 7 `÷` 3

7 Without using your calculator, find out which calculator operation **a** to **f** can be used to work out each of the calculations (i) to (iv).

a `AC` 43 `+` 9 `÷` 6 `=`

b `AC` 43 `+` 9 `=` `÷` 6 `=`

c `AC` 43 `÷` 6 `+` 9 `=`

d `AC` `(` 43 `+` 9 `)` `÷` 6 `=`

e `AC` 43 `÷` `(` 6 `+` 9 `)` `=`

f `AC` 43 `÷` 6 `=` `+` 9 `=`

(i) $\frac{43+9}{6}$ (ii) $43 + \frac{9}{6}$ (iii) $\frac{43}{6+9}$ (iv) $\frac{43}{6} + 9$

Check each of your answers with your calculator.

MASTERMINDERS

8 ▦ Work out, to 3 SF:

a $\sqrt{2.4^2 - 2.4 + 2.4 \times 2.4 \div (2.4 + 2.4)}$ **b** $680 \div \sqrt{\frac{6.8 + 8.6}{8.6 - 6.8}}$

9 Copy and complete the following by placing the correct digit in each $\square$:

a $76 \times 9\square = 7\square\square 0$

b $4\square\square \times \square 6 = 26\,544$

c $6408 \div 8\square = \square\square$

d $56\square \times \square 9 = 44\,319$

e $\square\square 8 \times 12\square = 46\,182$

10 Copy and complete the following by placing the correct sign in each $\square$:

a $42 \ \square \ 19 \ \square \ 202 = 1000$

b $28 \ \square \ 32 \ \square \ 21 = 700$

c $(3501 \ \square \ 279) \ \square \ 108 = 35$

Briefly describe your method.

__ Problem solving

__ Exercise 13

1 ▦ The newspaper printing plant at Wapping, London, prints 7 570 800 newspapers in 7.5 hours. Find the mean number printed, to 1 SF: **a** per hour **b** per minute **c** per second.

2 ▦ In the 1980s, the British Government spent about £18 000 million each year on defence. If the population was 55.5 million, find, to 2 SF, the mean cost of defence to each person per year.

3 ▦ To raise money for a charity, six million people joined hands to form a human chain across America. If the length of the chain was 6325 km, what was the mean link length per person? Give your answer in metres to 1 DP.

4 ▦ The River Amazon is 6448 km long and, on average, the water descends through a vertical height of 1 m every 1.25 km. Find the height, in metres to 2 SF, of the source above sea level.

5 ▦ Since they were built Concordes have flown 18 million km.
   a If the mean distance per flight was 3750 km, how many flights have they made?
   b If 439 200 passengers have travelled on Concorde, what is the mean number of passengers per flight?

6 ▦ Three sizes of Christmas card are printed on a school printing press. The numbers sold and the cost of each size are shown on the table. The total cost of production was £42.96.
Calculate:
   a The total profit.
   b The mean profit per card sold, to the nearest penny.

Size	Number sold	Selling price per card
Small	68	28p
Medium	142	37p
Large	51	56p

MASTERMINDERS

7 ▦ A car hire firm rents out small and large cars for weekly hire. To hire a small car, a deposit of £100 must be paid, together with a distance charge of 20p per mile. The petrol for a small car costs 8p per mile.
To hire a large car, a deposit of £100 must be paid, together with a distance charge of 25p per mile. The petrol for a large car costs 10p per mile.
Two men, one with a large car and one with a small car, find that they both have to pay £240 at the end of the week. Find the distance each travelled.

8 ▦ At the beginning of the summer a reservoir was full and contained 75 million m³ of water. After a 60-day summer period, when there was no rain, the reservoir was only half full. If it supplied a town with a population of 250 000, find the mean amount of water used (in litres) by each person per day through this period.

9 ▦ The Caspian Sea is the largest inland sea in the world, but it is slowly drying up. Over the last 50 years it has had a mean surface area of 378 000 km^2, but its water level has dropped by 18.25 m.

  a Calculate the mean volume of water which has evaporated per second. (1 year = 365 days).

  b Between now and the time when the Sea dries up, the mean surface area can be taken to be half the above figure. If the Sea is 876 m deep, after how many years will it have dried up?

1.6 Percentages

The value of a percentage is the same as the numerator of a fraction whose denominator is 100, because the **unit** for comparison is **one hundred**.

For example, $15\% = \dfrac{15}{100}$

REMEMBER

In percentages the unit for comparison is 100.

Activity 3

We are going to explore percentages which are less than 100%, and greater than 100%.

Suppose that British Rail has announced a 20% increase in long-distance rail fares. Last year it cost £80 to travel from Paddington to York. How much more will it cost this year?

In this example, the original cost (£80) is taken to be 100%.

1   The fare increase is 20% of £80.

$$20\% \text{ of } £80 = \frac{20}{100} \times £80 = £16$$

Copy and complete the following table for other percentages of £80.

%	0	20	40	60	80	100
£		16				80

2   These figures can be illustrated on a 'ratio line', as shown here:

```
0%      20%     40%     60%     80%     100%
+-------+-------+-------+-------+-------+------->
£0      £16     £32     £48     £64     £80
```

(Continued)

Copy the ratio line on page 25 and extend it to 200%. Work out, and write on your ratio line, the number of £s which represent 120%, 140%, 160%, 180% and 200%.

3 Use your ratio line to work out, as a percentage, how much:
a £64 is less than £80   **b** £48 is less than £80
c £96 is more than £80   **d** £112 is more than £80.

It is important to note that:

$$\frac{20}{16} = \frac{40}{32} = \frac{60}{48} = \frac{80}{64} = \frac{100}{80} = \frac{120}{96} = \frac{140}{112} = \frac{160}{128} = \frac{180}{144} = \frac{200}{160}$$

REMEMBER

When finding a percentage of a quantity:
- A percentage less than 100% decreases a quantity.
- A percentage greater than 100% increases a quantity.

___ Exercise 14

1 What is:
a 90% of £20   **b** 100% of £20   **c** 110% of £20   **d** 150% of £20?

2 What is:
a 80% of 60 m   **b** 95% of 60 m   **c** 120% of 60 m   **d** 200% of 60 m?

3  What is:
a 109% of 5.8 km   **b** 114% of 87.5 kg,   **c** 175% of 8.3 m², **d** 235% of 0.6 cm?

4 Which is greater and by how much: **a** 138% of 6 miles   **b** 194% of 4.2 miles?

5 What is: **a** 101% of 40 kg   **b** 1% of 40 kg? Comment on your answers.

6 Taking £120 to be 100%, find
a 75% of £120   **b** 150% of £120.

Copy and complete this ratio line:

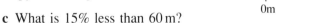

c What is 25% less than £120?
b What is 50% more than £120?

7 Taking 60 m to be 100%, find
a 85% of 60 m   **b** 105% of 60 m.

Copy and complete this ratio line:

c What is 15% less than 60 m?
d What is 5% more than 60 m?

Revision Exercise 1A

Calculators are **not allowed** for Questions 1 to 7.

1 Work out: **a** $78.2 - 9.5$ **b** 34×0.6 **b** $16.32 \div 8$ **d** 1.06×0.12

2 Change to a mixed number: **a** $\frac{9}{4}$ **b** $\frac{13}{3}$ **c** $\frac{26}{5}$

3 Change to a decimal: **a** $\frac{2}{5}$ **b** $\frac{3}{30}$ **c** $\frac{1}{6}$

4 Work out: **a** $2\frac{1}{2} + 3\frac{1}{6}$ **b** $4\frac{5}{8} - 2\frac{1}{2}$ **c** $2\frac{1}{4} \times \frac{2}{3}$ **d** $4\frac{1}{2} \div 1\frac{1}{2}$

5 Five thirteenths of all the books in a library are fiction.
  a What fraction are not fiction?
  b If there is a total of 3900 books in the library, how many are fiction?

6 Work out: **a** $(-2) + (-5)$ **b** $10 - (-3)$ **c** $(-4) \times (6)$ **d** $(-12) \div (-4)$

7 Correct 29.856 to: **a** 2 SF **b** 2 DP.

8 ▦ Use your calculator to work out: **a** $\frac{5.86 - 1.61}{1.7}$ **b** $\frac{3}{7} \times 8.68$

9 ▦ Use your calculator to work out, correct to 3 SF:
  a $\sqrt{8} + 3$ **b** $\left(\frac{2.1}{4.9}\right)^2$

10 ▦ Work out 115% of £99.

Revision Exercise 1B

Calculators are **not allowed** for Questions 1 to 9.

1 Work out: **a** $12.3 - 34.6 + 9.8$ **b** 78.9×7 **c** 0.95×0.04 **d** $14.1 \div 15$

2 Change $\frac{3}{8}$ to a decimal.

3 Change 0.26 to a fraction in its simplest form.

4 Change $\frac{3}{11}$ to a recurring decimal.

5 Work out: **a** $2\frac{7}{8} + 1\frac{2}{3}$ **b** $3\frac{3}{4} - 2\frac{2}{3}$ **c** $2\frac{8}{9} \times \frac{12}{13}$ **d** $2\frac{4}{15} \div 1\frac{7}{10}$

6 In a library there are 12 600 books. Five sevenths of the books are fiction, one sixth are reference. How many are neither fiction nor reference?

7 Work out: **a** $(-6) - (-2)$ **b** $(-6) \div (-3)$ **c** $(-6) + (-6)$ **d** $(-6) \times (-5)$

8 Correct to 3 SF: **a** 70 948 **b** 0.017 851

9 Correct to 2 DP: **a** 1.006 **b** 12.797

10 ▦ Use your calculator to work out, correct to 2 SF:
  a $38.9 \div (98.7 - 89.8)$
  b $\frac{5}{61}$
  c $\frac{20.5}{9.7} - 4.8$
  d 2.5×4.8^2
  e $\frac{3.09}{2.89 - 4.76}$
  f $\sqrt{\frac{96}{43}}$

11 ▦ Which is larger and by how much, 134% of £67 or 118% of £76?

___ Basics Test 1

A Calculator
Write each answer correct to 3 SF.

1 $\frac{3.96 + 2.96}{1.96}$ **2** $\frac{3.96}{1.96} + 2.96$ **3** $\frac{3.96}{1.96 + 2.96}$

4 $21.1^2 - 48.2$ **5** $(68.2 - 4.03) \times 7$ **6** $1 \div (9.8 + 7.4)$

B Paper and pencil

7 $15.9 - 9.8 + 0.786$ **8** 12.8×0.76 **9** $\frac{3}{4} \times 1\frac{5}{7}$

10 $\frac{2}{3} - \frac{1}{4}$ **11** $\frac{4}{15} \div \frac{2}{5}$ **12** $3\frac{1}{7} + 2\frac{1}{3}$

13 Change $\frac{3}{11}$ to a recurring decimal.

14 Change $\frac{87}{12}$ to a mixed number.

15 What percentage of 75 is 15?

C Mental
Ten questions will be read out to you.
You need the following facts to answer Questions 16 to 20.
A packet of crisps costs 16p. A tin of Coke costs 44p.

___ Puzzlers

1 Make four triangles using only six matches. No match may be placed across another.

2 From a piece of paper, cut out a strip about 30 cm long and 3 cm wide.

A [====================================] D
B [====================================] C

a Make your strip into a paper ring with a single twist, by glueing A onto C and D onto B. Carefully cut along the centre line of your ring. Comment on the result.

b Repeat part **a** but this time cut along the broken lines as shown in the diagram. What do you notice?

c **Investigate** what happens if two twists are put into your ring.

3 Copy and complete the following by inserting the correct sign in each box. There are two possible answers for part **b** (i) and three for part **b** (ii).

a (i) $\frac{2}{5} \ \square \ \frac{1}{4} \ \square \ \frac{1}{2} = \frac{3}{20}$ **b** (i) $\frac{1}{3} \ \square \ \frac{1}{4} \ \square \ \frac{1}{5} = \frac{23}{60}$

(ii) $\frac{2}{5} \ \square \ \frac{1}{4} \ \square \ \frac{1}{2} = \frac{1}{20}$ (ii) $\frac{1}{3} \ \square \ \frac{1}{4} \ \square \ \frac{1}{5} = \frac{17}{60}$

(iii) $\frac{2}{5} \ \square \ \frac{1}{4} \ \square \ \frac{1}{2} = \frac{1}{5}$ (iii) $\frac{1}{3} \ \square \ \frac{1}{4} \ \square \ \frac{1}{5} = -\frac{7}{60}$

c (i) $1.05 \ \square \ 0.98 \ \square \ 0.84 = 1.225$ **d** (i) $0.98 \ \square \ 0.84 \ \square \ 1.05 = 0.784$

(ii) $1.05 \ \square \ 0.98 \ \square \ 0.84 = 1.19$ (ii) $0.98 \ \square \ 0.84 \ \square \ 1.05 = 0.77$

Coursework: Protein yield

Protein is an essential part of our diet. It is found in foods such as vegetables, beef, eggs, potatoes and wheat. Table 1 shows the amount of protein which can be produced on 1 hectare in a year from five different agricultural products.

(A square of side 100 m has an area of 1 hectare (ha).)

	Vegetables	Beef	Eggs	Potatoes	Wheat
Protein	840 kg	56 kg	168 kg	560 kg	336 kg

Table 1

1 Illustrate the values in Table 1 on a clearly labelled bar chart.

2 A farmer grows vegetables on a field of area 1 hectare, and he produces 840 kg of protein each year.

  a Show that to produce 840 kg of protein from beef cattle in a year, a farmer would require 15 hectares of land. Copy and complete Table 2.

	Vegetables	Beef	Eggs	Potatoes	Wheat
Area of land to produce 840 kg of protein	1 ha	15 ha			
	Total area = ? hectares				

Table 2

  b This diagram represents a 25 hectare field. Each square represents 1 hectare. Copy this diagram and use it to illustrate the figures in part **a**. (1 square represents vegetables.) Comment.

3 The average human requires 28 kg of protein a year.
Vegetables are grown on 1 hectare of land. Show that this would produce enough protein in a year for 30 humans. Perform similar calculations if 1 hectare of land is used to produce protein from each of the other four products. Copy Table 3 and enter your results. Comment.

	Vegetables	Beef	Eggs	Potatoes	Wheat
No. of humans	30				

Table 3

EXTENSION

4 England has a population of 50 million and a land area of 130 000 km². **Investigate** the problem of relying only on home-produced beef to satisfy the country's protein requirement.

2 ALGEBRA I

2.1 Basic principles

Read carefully through these Examples to remind yourself of the basic principles of Algebra – simplifying, substituting and their use in solving equations – which were covered in Book 1.

> *REMEMBER*
>
> When simplifying: only 'like terms' can be added and subtracted.

■ *EXAMPLE 1*

Simplify: **a** $3m + 4n - 2m + 3n$ **b** $2p + 10 - p - 3$

a $3m + 4n - 2m + 3n$ (Arrange like terms together)
   $= 3m - 2m + 4n + 3n$
   $= m + 7n$

b $2p + 10 - p - 3$ (Arrange like terms together)
   $= 2p - p + 10 - 3$
   $= p + 7$

■ *EXAMPLE 2*

If $x = 3$ and $y = 2$, find the value of: **a** $\frac{x}{y} + x$ **b** $xy - y$

a [F] $x = 3, y = 2$
   [E] $\frac{x}{y} + x$
   [S] $= \frac{3}{2} + 3$
   [W] $= 1\frac{1}{2} + 3 = 4\frac{1}{2}$

b [F] $x = 3, y = 2$
   [E] $xy - y$
   [S] $= 3 \times 2 - 2$
   [W] $= 6 - 2 = 4$

> *REMEMBER*
>
> When substituting:
> 1 Write down the **facts**.   [F]
> 2 Write down the **expression**.   [E]
> 3 **Substitute** the facts.   [S]
> 4 Finally, do the **working**.   [W]

In Book 1, you learnt how to solve six basic types of equation. Read Example 3 through carefully to remind yourself of each type.

> *REMEMBER*
>
> When solving equations: you must do the **same operation to both sides of the equation**

■ *EXAMPLE 3*

Solve each of the following equations:

a $q + 4 = 12$ **b** $r - 15 = 12$ **c** $3s = 39$ **d** $\frac{t}{3} = 7$ **e** $4 = \frac{12}{p}$ **f** $5 = 10 - v$

a $q + 4 = 12$ (Subtract 4 from both sides) **b** $r - 15 = 12$ (Add 15 to both sides)
$\quad q = 12 - 4$ $\qquad\qquad\qquad\qquad\qquad\qquad r = 12 + 15$
$\quad q = 8$ $\qquad\qquad\qquad\qquad\qquad\qquad\qquad r = 27$

c $\quad 3s = 39$ (Divide both sides by 3) **d** $\qquad \frac{t}{3} = 7$ (Multiply both sides by 3)
$\quad s = \frac{39}{3}$ $\qquad\qquad\qquad\qquad\qquad\qquad t = 7 \times 3$
$\quad s = 13$ $\qquad\qquad\qquad\qquad\qquad\qquad\quad t = 21$

e $\quad 4 = \frac{12}{p}$ (Multiply both sides by p) **f** $\qquad 5 = 10 - v$ (Add v to both sides)
$\quad 4p = 12$ (Divide both sides by 4) $\qquad\qquad v + 5 = 10$ (Subtract 5 from both sides)
$\quad p = \frac{12}{4}$ $\qquad\qquad\qquad\qquad\qquad\qquad\quad v = 10 - 5$
$\quad p = 3$ $\qquad\qquad\qquad\qquad\qquad\qquad\qquad v = 5$

___ Exercise 15

1 ▦ If $p = 2.4$ and $q = 0.6$, find the value of:
    a $p + q$ **b** $p - q$ **c** $2p + q$ **d** $4p - q$
    e $p + 6q$ **f** $p - 2q$ **g** $4p + 5q$ **h** $7p - 8q$

2 If $m = 2\frac{1}{2}$ and $n = 1\frac{1}{2}$, find the value of:
    a $\frac{m+n}{m}$ **b** $\frac{m-n}{m}$ **c** $\frac{3m+n}{n}$ **d** $\frac{6m-5n}{n}$
    e $\frac{m}{m+n}$ **f** $\frac{4m}{m-n}$ **g** $\frac{6n}{3m+n}$ **h** $\frac{2n}{5m-3n}$

3 ▦ If $u = 0.5$ and $v = 0.025$, find the value of:
    a $4u$ **b** $100v$ **c** $\frac{6}{u}$ **d** $\frac{20}{v}$
    e $30uv$ **f** $\frac{u}{v}$ **g** $\frac{u}{4v}$ **h** $\frac{15v}{u}$

4 Simplify by collecting like terms:
    a $4x + 2y + 6x + 7y$ **b** $12m + 5n - 5m + 11n + 8m$ **c** $10v + 9w + 2v - 8w + 6w$
    d $8p - 9q + 12p + 30q$ **e** $20r + 24s - 6r - 9s$ **f** $19y + 21z - 11y - 12z$
    g $2p + 9q + 7r + q + 7p + 5r$ **h** $16t + u + 20v - 8t - 11v + 9u$

5 Simplify by collecting like terms:
    a $8x + 10 + 10x + 15$ **b** $12y + 16 + 3y - 15$ **c** $15z - 40 + 6z + 45$
    d $30t + 24 - 14t - 21$ **e** $24u + 15 - 3u - 7$ **f** $10v + 15 + 6 - 2v$
    g $21 - 14p + 18p + 6$ **h** $18 + 21q - 10 - 12q$

6 Simplify each expression and then find its value when $r = \frac{1}{2}$ and $s = 2$:
    a $10r - 2s + 2r$ **b** $10s + 60r - 9s$ **c** $12s - 20r - 2s$
    d $12r + 18s - 4r$ **e** $2r + 2s + 10r + 5s$ **f** $20r - 4s + 12r + 3s$
    g $6r + 12s + 24r - 2s$ **h** $20r + 15s - 48r - 3s$

For Questions 7–11, find which, of equations **a**, **b** and **c**, has a different answer from the other two.

7 a $x + 7 = 25$ **b** $x + 35 = 51$ **c** $9 + x = 27$

8 a $y - 13 = 32$ **b** $19 = y - 29$ **c** $60 - y = 12$

9 a $32 - z = 8$ **b** $6z = 144$ **c** $252 = 9z$

10 a $480 = 15p$ **b** $\frac{p}{3} = 12$ **c** $7.2 = \frac{p}{5}$

11 a $\frac{20}{t} = 4$ **b** $15 = \frac{90}{t}$ **c** $\frac{105}{t} = 21$

___ 2.2 Symbolic expression

'Symbolic expression' is the process of writing a mathematical statement which includes a letter or a number of letters. For example, if we are told that Jill is 10 years old and that her father is x years older, then we can write that her father is $(x + 10)$ years old: we have produced a 'symbolic expression'.

■ *EXAMPLE 1*

How many stamps which cost 15p can be bought for **a** £3 **b** £x?

a   Number of stamps for £3 $= \dfrac{100 \times 3}{15} = 20$

b   Number of stamps for £$x = \dfrac{100x}{15} = \dfrac{20x}{3}$

___ Exercise 16

1   How many pence are there in **a** £6 **b** £x?

2   How many centimetres are there in **a** 5 metres **b** y metres?

3   How many millimetres are there in **a** 8 metres **b** z metres?

4   How many kilograms are there in **a** 4 tonnes **b** t tonnes?

5   Find the cost of: **a** 3 records at £4 each **b** 3 records at £y each **c** m records at £4 each **d** m records at £y each.

6   **a** A boy is three times as old as his cat. If his cat is five years old, how old is the boy?
       b Another boy is m times older than his dog. If his dog is t years old, how old is this boy?

7   **a** By how much is 30 bigger than 23?   **b** By how much is 23 bigger than q?
       c By how much is u bigger than v?   **d** By how much is x smaller than 55?
       e By how much is 55 smaller than y?   **f** By how much is n smaller than m?

8 a Sarah has five more sweets than Anne. If Anne has x, how many has Sarah?
  b Tariq has seven fewer chocolates than Paul. If Paul has y, how many has Tariq?

9 a Peter has four pens. Maggie has p more. How many has Maggie?
  b Tom has eight pencils. Naseem has q fewer. How many has Naseem?

10 a For the rectangle illustrated, find (i) the area (in both cm^2
    and mm^2) (ii) the perimeter (in both cm and mm).
  b For the right-angled triangle illustrated, find (i) the area (in
    both m^2 and cm^2) (ii) the perimeter (in both m and cm).

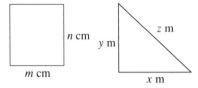

11 a If a cricketer scores m runs in p matches, what is his average score per match?
  b If a footballer plays in n matches one season and scores an average of t goals per match, how
    many goals did he score over the whole season?

12 a 6 apples cost x pence. Find the cost of: (i) 1 apple (ii) 5 apples (iii) m apples
    (iv) $5m$ apples.
  b n pears cost 30p. Find the cost of: (i) 1 pear (ii) 4 pears (iii) x pears (iv) $4x$ pears.

13 a How many stamps costing x pence each could be bought for (i) £2 (ii) £m?
  b Loaves of bread cost y pence each. How many loaves does Mrs Jones buy if she spends
    (i) £5 (ii) £n, on loaves?

14 Find the average of each of the following:
  a m, n, p and q **b** u, v, w, x, y and z **c** t, $4t$, $7t$, $5t$ and $3t$.

MASTERMINDERS

15 Westcoastville and Eastcoastville are x km apart.
  a Find my average speed, if it takes me five hours
    to walk from one to the other.
  b Find my brother's average speed if it takes him
    m hours to cycle from one to the other.

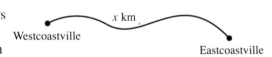

  c Find the time my father takes to drive from one to the other, if the average speed of his car
    is 50 km/h.
  d Find the time that a bus journey between the two places takes, if the average speed of the bus
    is p km/h.

16 A coach journey costs r pence for a distance of x kilometres. If the same rate is charged per
  kilometre, what is the cost of a journey of (i) 30 km (ii) y km?

17 A quantity of rubble to be moved consists of r tonnes. The lorry clearing the rubble can move x
  tonnes on each journey and can make n journeys per day. Find : **a** the amount moved per day
  b the number of days required to clear the rubble **c** the amount moved after u days.

18 s tonnes of coal are to be moved from a colliery to a power station. The train which moves
  the coal can carry y tonnes on each journey, and can make m journeys per day. Find:
  a the total number of journeys required **b** the number of days required to move the coal
  c the amount moved and the amount remaining after v days.

__ 2.3 Brackets

── REMEMBER

$3b = b + b + b = 3 \times b$

It therefore follows that: $3(b + 2) = b + 2 + b + 2 + b + 2 = 3b + 6$

Note that the term outside the bracket has multiplied **each of the terms inside**. Aways remember this when brackets are removed.

■ *EXAMPLE 1*

For each of the following, remove the brackets and, where possible, simplify by collecting like terms: **a** $3(x + 2y)$ **b** $4(u - v) + 3u$ **c** $4m + 3(m - 2n)$ **d** $3r - (s + 2r)$

a $3(x + 2y)$
  $= 3x + 6y$

b $4(u - v) + 3u$
  $= 4u - 4v + 3u$
  $= 7u - 4v$

c $4m + 3(m - 2n)$
  $= 4m + 3m - 6n$
  $= 7m - 6n$

d $3r - (s + 2r)$
  $= 3r - 1(s + 2r)*$
  $= 3r - s - 2r$
  $= r - s$

*Note that in part **d** a figure '1' was placed outside the bracket. This can be helpful. Also notice that the negative sign **outside** the bracket has changed all the signs inside.

__ Exercise 17

For each of the following, remove the brackets and where possible simplify by collecting like terms:

1 $5(m + n)$	**2** $3(a + 4)$	**3** $7(2 + 3p)$	**4** $2(b - 4c)$
5 $4(d - 5)$	**6** $8(3 - 2q)$	**7** $a(b + c)$	**8** $x(3y + 2)$
9 $u(4 + v)$	**10** $m(n - 2p)$	**11** $r(s - 7)$	**12** $a(9 - 4b)$
13 $-2(c + 7)$	**14** $-3(m - 3)$	**15** $-4(9 - 5n)$	**16** $2(x + y) + 7x$
17 $4(2p + q) + 5q$	**18** $5(m - n) - 3m$	**19** $9(a + 3b) - 4b$	**20** $7(u - v) + 13v$
21 $3(y + 5) + 4y$	**22** $6(3u + 4) - 5u$	**23** $5(z + 7) + 9$	**24** $4(2t - 7) + 35$
25 $3(v - 5) - 7$	**26** $9m - 2(m + 2n)$	**27** $11x - 3(3x + 5)$	**28** $7y - (y + 7)$

29 $15 - 2(4t + 3)$ **30** $12 - (3z + 2)$ **31** $3(x + 4y) + 5(2x + 3y)$

32 $4(3y + 5) + 3(y - 3)$ **33** $11(a + 2) + 5(3 - a)$ **34** $5(2 + 5t) + 9(1 - 2t)$

MASTERMINDERS

35 $q - q(p - q) + pq$ **36** $(y + x) - (x - y) + (y - x) - (x + y)$

37 $x(y + z) + y(x + z) - z(x + y)$ **38** $a(a - b) + b(a + b) - a(a + b) + b(a - b)$

— 2.4 Substitution

When a number of different operations have to be worked out in one calculation, remember B I D M A S (page 20).

Set out each substitution using [F], [E], [S], [W].

> **REMEMBER**
>
> $3a^2$ means $3 \times a \times a = 3 \times a^2$
>
> $(3a)^2$ means $3a \times 3a = 9a^2$

■ EXAMPLE 1

If $p = 4$ and $q = 1.5$, find the value of each of the following:

a $3p^2$ **b** $(3p)^2$ **c** $5(2p - q) - 3(p + q)$

a   [F] $p = 4, q = 1.5$ **b**   [F] $p = 4, q = 1.5$

      [E] $3p^2$ [E] $(3p)^2$

      [S] $= 3 \times 4^2$ [S] $= (3 \times 4)^2$

      [W] $= 3 \times 4 \times 4 = 48$ [W] $= 12 \times 12 = 144$

c   This can be worked out in different ways. (Substitute first.)

      [F] $p = 4, q = 1.5$

      [E] $5(2p - q) - 3(p + q)$

      [S] $= 5(2 \times 4 - 1.5) - 3(4 + 1.5)$

      [W] $= 5 \times 6.5 - 3 \times 5.5$

               $= 32.5 - 16.5 = 16$

      (Or, simplify first, and then substitute.)

      [E] $5(2p - q) - 3(p + q)$

               $= 10p - 5q - 3p - 3q$

               $= 7p - 8q$

      [S] $= 7 \times 4 - 8 \times 1.5$

      [W] $= 28 - 12 = 16$

Exercise 18

1 Find the value of $4x^2$ if x is equal to:

   a 3   **b** 0.5   **c** $\frac{3}{4}$ **d** 2.5

2 Find the value of $(4x)^2$, if x is equal to:

   a 3   **b** 0.5   **c** $\frac{3}{4}$ **d** 2.5

3 If $y = 8$, find the value of:

   a $2y^2$ **b** $(2y)^2$ **c** $(y + 2)^2$ **d** $(y - 2)^2$

   e $\frac{y^2}{2}$ **f** $\left(\frac{y}{2}\right)^2$

4 If $z = 2.5$, find the value of:

   a $(2z + 3)^2$ **b** $(4z - 5)^2$ **c** $(4 - z)^2$ **d** $z(z + 1.5)$

   e $2z(z + 4)$ **f** $2z(3z - 3.5)$

5 If $t = 4$, find the value of:

   a $3(t + 5) + 4$ **b** $2(4t + 3) - 5$ **c** $4(2t - 1) + 7$ **d** $3(10 - t) + 6$

   e $5(t - 2) - 3$ **f** $2(16 - 3t) - 4$

6 If $u = 1.5$, find the value of:

   a $2(u + 0.5) + 4u$ **b** $3(2u + 5) - 3u$ **c** $5(3u - 2) + 2u$ **d** $10(u - 0.5) - 3u$

   e $2(4.5 - u) + 8u$ **f** $4(7 - 3u) - 5u$

7 If $v = 3$, find the value of:

   a $16v - 2(3v + 1)$ **b** $23 - (5v + 7)$ **c** $26 - 2(v^2 + 3)$ **d** $14v^2 - 4(3v^2 + 2)$

   e $5v^2 + 5(4v^2 + 3)$ **f** $9 + 3(2v^2 + 3)$

8 If $p = 2$, and $q = 5$, find the value of:

   a pq **b** pq^2 **c** p^2q **d** $p^2 + q^2$ **e** $(p + q)^2$

9 **a** Find the perimeter and area of the rectangle if $x = 6$.

   b Find the perimeter and area of the rectangle if $x = 4.5$.

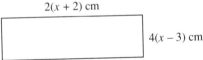

$2(x + 2)$ cm

$4(x - 3)$ cm

10 A car is bought for £$40(x + 15)$ and sold for £$45(x + 20)$. What is the profit if $x = 10$?

11 This map shows the route taken by a bus from Darlington to Hawes.

The table below shows the distance and the time taken by the bus between adjacent places.

Section of route	Distance (km)	Time (minutes)
Darlington to Richmond	$4(2p + 1)$	$9(q + 1)$
Richmond to Leyburn	$6(2p - 1)$	$5(2q + 1)$
Leyburn to Hawes	$9(p + 1)$	$4(4q - 1)$

Darlington

Richmond

Leyburn

Hawes

If $p = 2$ and $q = 4$, find: **a** the total distance from Darlington to Hawes   **b** the total journey time   **c** the average speed of the bus over the whole journey.

12 A garage buys an old car for £12(2x + 3) and sells it for £7(x − 4). What profit does it make if x = 120?

13 a Find the area and perimeter of the triangle if p = 4.
b Find the angles of the triangle if x = 6.

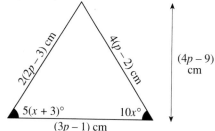

2(2p − 3) cm   4(p − 2) cm   (4p − 9) cm

5(x + 3)°   10x°

(3p − 1) cm

MASTERMINDERS

14 One day Howard travels from his house to his school and the whole journey takes one hour. Further details of his journey are as follows.

He takes 2(t + 3) minutes to walk to the bus stop where he waits 3(4t − 3) minutes for the bus.
His bus journey takes 6(t + 3) minutes and after he gets off the bus, it takes him 5(2t − 3) minutes to walk to his school.

Find the value of t and each of the four times given above.

15 Pat, Liz and Jill are three sisters. Their mean height is 100 cm. Further details of their heights are as follows.

Pat is 2(x + 24) cm tall,
Liz is 5(3x − 8) cm tall,
and Jill is 8(x − 1) cm tall.

Find the value of x and the height of each of the three girls.

16 ▦ Work out each of the following, where v = 3.875.

a $\dfrac{v + v + v + v + v + v}{6}$

b $\dfrac{v + v + v + v + v + v}{v}$

Comment on your answers.

17 When a = −2 and b = −3, find the value of:
a $2a^2 - b$
b $(2a)^2 - b$
c $2(a^2 - b)$

— 2.5 Equations

You need to be able to solve the six basic equations, reviewed in Example 3 on page 31, before attempting this section.

REMEMBER

When solving equations: you must do the **same operation to both sides.**

■ *EXAMPLE 1*

Solve: **a** $3x - 4 = 11$ **b** $\frac{y}{5} + 2 = 7$ **c** $11 - 3z = 5$ **d** $\frac{15}{t} + 3 = 8$

a $3x - 4 = 11$ (Add 4 to both sides)

$\qquad 3x = 15$ (Divide both sides by 3)

$\qquad x = 5$

b $\dfrac{y}{5} + 2 = 7$ (Subtract 2 from both sides)

$\qquad \dfrac{y}{5} = 5$ (Multiply both sides by 5)

$\qquad y = 25$

c $11 - 3z = 5$ (Add $3z$ to both sides)

$\qquad 11 = 5 + 3z$ (Subtract 5 from both sides)

$\qquad 6 = 3z$ (Divide both sides by 3)

$\qquad 2 = z$ or $z = 2$

d $\dfrac{15}{t} + 3 = 8$ (Subtract 3 from both sides)

$\qquad \dfrac{15}{t} = 5$ (Multiply both sides by t)

$\qquad 15 = 5t$ (Divide both sides by 5)

$\qquad 3 = t$ or $t = 3$

REMEMBER

When solving equations: first collect up the **like terms** on either side of the equals sign.

— Exercise 19

Find which, of equations **a**, **b** and **c**, has a different answer from the other two.

1   **a** $3x + 7 = 25$ **b** $5x + 13 = 48$ **c** $4x + 9 = 33$

2   **a** $17 + 5y = 72$ **b** $55 + 12y = 199$ **c** $9y - 16 = 92$

3   **a** $7z - 24 = 39$ **b** $8z - 49 = 15$ **c** $48 = 11z - 51$

4   **a** $51 - 2t = 15$ **b** $75 - 4t = 11$ **c** $110 - 3t = 56$

5   **a** $32 = 200 - 7u$ **b** $180 = 300 - 5u$ **c** $\frac{u}{4} + 16 = 21$

6   **a** $\frac{v}{15} + 8 = 13$ **b** $33 + \frac{v}{6} = 45$ **c** $\frac{v}{8} - 3 = 6$

7   **a** $10 - \frac{q}{12} = 2$ **b** $60 - \frac{q}{6} = 45$ **c** $16 = 40 - \frac{q}{4}$

MASTERMINDERS

8   **a** $\frac{2}{3}x = 24$ **b** $\frac{3}{4}x + 18 = 45$ **c** $\frac{5}{6}x - 19 = 6$

9   **a** $40 - \frac{120}{t} = 25$ **b** $14 - \frac{35}{t} = 9$ **c** $35 = 60 - \frac{175}{t}$

— 2.6 Problem solving

In this section you will use equations to solve problems. In each case, a letter is used to represent the unknown number.

■ *EXAMPLE 1*

Diana has x pencils and Susan has three times as many.

a   Write down, in terms of x, the number of pencils which Susan has.

b   If, between them, they have a total of 24, write down an equation and solve it for x.

c   Use your answer to find the number of pencils that each girl has.

a   Susan has $3x$ pencils.

b   [F]   Diana: x pencils.   Susan: $3x$ pencils.   Total: 24 pencils.

     [E] and [S] $x + 3x = 24$

     [W] $4x = 24$

                   $x = 6$

c   Diana has 6 pencils, Susan has $3 \times 6 = 18$ pencils.

     REMEMBER

       Always write down **all** the facts in a 'mathematical way', before you write the equation.

■ *EXAMPLE 2*

Jake and David each have a mass of m kg. Katia, Wendy and Alison each have 5 kg less mass.
a   Write down, in terms of m, the mass of each girl.
b   If the total mass of all five is 210 kg, write down an equation and solve it for m.
c   Find the mass of each of the boys and each of the girls.

a   Mass of each girl $= (m - 5)$ kg

b   [F]   Two boys have a mass of $2m$ kg. Three girls have a mass of $3(m - 5)$ kg.
                  Total mass $= 210$ kg.
   [E] and [S] $2m + 3(m - 5) = 210$
   [W] $2m + 3m - 15 = 210$
                  $$5m = 210 + 15$$
                  $$m = \frac{225}{5}$$
                  $$m = 45$$

c   Each boy has a mass of 45 kg.
    Each girl has a mass of $(45 - 5) = 40$ kg.

___ Exercise 20

1   The diagram represents a rectangular room.
    a Write down, in terms of x, the perimeter of the room.
    b If the perimeter is 72 metres, write down an equation
    and solve it for x.
    c Find the length and width of the room.

5x metres

7x metres

2   Janet receives £x a week pocket money. Her sister, Lucy, receives twice as much.
    a Write down, in terms of x, the amount Lucy receives.
    b If the two of them receive a total of £15 a week, write down an equation and solve it for x.
    c Find how much each girl receives.

3   Bob has a mass of m kg. His father has three times as much mass. Gerry has a mass of 20 kg.
    a Write down, in terms of m, the mass of Bob's father.
    b If the total mass of all three is 110 kg, write down an equation and solve it for m.
    c Find the mass of Bob's father.

4   In the isosceles triangle ABC, the length AB is 3 cm
    more than CB.
    a Write down, in terms of y, the length of AB.
    b If the perimeter is 27 cm, write down an equation
      and solve it for y.
    c Find the length of AC.

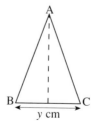

A

B y cm   C

5   A rectangle has a perimeter of 28 cm. If it is x cm long and $(x - 4)$ cm wide, write an equation
    involving x and solve it to find the length of the rectangle.

6 Samir takes b pence to a Fair but after having a turn on all the rides he likes, he has only one third of his money left. He then, however, wins 60p from a gaming machine and finds that he has £2.40. How much did he have originally?

7 Mikhail has x marbles. He wins one game and finds that he has four times as many, but he then loses 15 in another game and finds that he has 17 left. How many did he have originally?

MASTERMINDERS

8 Look at this map.

a Find the time that a train takes to travel from Newcastle to Carlisle, given that it takes only one third of this time to reach Hexham; it arrives at Haltwhistle 25 minutes later, having then travelled for 55 minutes from Newcastle.

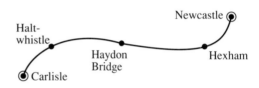

b Find the time I take to drive from Newcastle to Carlisle, given that I pass Haydon Bridge after one half of this time has elapsed, and that this in turn is 15 minutes later than when I passed Hexham, 35 minutes after leaving Newcastle.

9 This window frame has a frontal surface area of 850 cm². Find:

a The value of x.
b The width of the frame.
c The value of t.

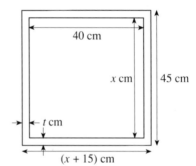

___ 2.7 Sequences

A series of numbers which follows a definite pattern is called a 'sequence'.

> ___ REMEMBER
>
> - To continue a sequence, look at the **difference** between the numbers.
> - To find the rule for a sequence, use a 'sequence table' (see next page).
> - Use the rule to produce the sequence.

Look carefully through the following Examples and work through the Activity to remind yourself of each of these skills.

■ *EXAMPLE 1*

Find the fifth and sixth terms of the sequence: 7, 10, 14, 19, . . .

The differences between each successive term are 3, 4, 5, . . .

$$7 \xrightarrow{+3} 10 \xrightarrow{+4} 14 \xrightarrow{+5} 19$$

Therefore the fifth term is $19 + 6 = 25$
and the sixth term is $25 + 7 = 32$.

■ *EXAMPLE 2*

In the sequence 3, 6, 9, 12, . . . find **a** the nth term   **b** the 40th term.

a   First draw up a 'sequence table' like this:

Term number (n)	1	2	3	4
Sequence	3	6	9	12

From the sequence table, each term in the sequence is three times larger than its term number:

$$3 \times 1 = 3 \quad 3 \times 2 = 6 \quad 3 \times 3 = 9 \quad 3 \times 4 = 12$$

Therefore the nth term is $3 \times n = 3n$.

b   When $n = 40$, $3n = 3 \times 40$.
Therefore the 40th term is $3 \times 40 = 120$.

___ *Activity 4*

1   If the nth term in a sequence is found from the rule $2n + 1$, show that the first four terms are:
3, 5, 7, 9.

Copy and complete the table.

	Term number (n)				Rule for nth term
	1	2	3	4	
a	3	5	7	9	$2n + 1$
b					$3n + 1$
c					$4n + 1$
d	4	6	8	10	
e	5	8	11	14	

	Term number (n)				Rule for nth term
	1	2	3	4	
f	6	10	14	18	
g	2	6	10	14	
h	1	5			$4n - \square$
i	0	4			$\square - 4$
j			7	11	$4n - \square$

2   Find the relationship between the number in front of the 'n' in the rule, and the difference between the numbers in the sequence.

3   Some sequences are generated by more complicated rules. For example, the rule $n^2 + 2$ generates the sequence 3, 6, 11, 18, . . .

Copy and complete the table on the opposite page.

	Term number (n)				Rule for nth term
	1	2	3	4	
a	3	6	11	18	$n^2 + 2$
b					$n^2 - 2$
c					$n^2 + 3$
d	5	8	13	20	
e					$2n^2 + 1$

	Term number (n)				Rule for nth term
	1	2	3	4	
f	4	10	20	34	
g	4	13			$3n^2 + \square$
h	0	2	6		$n^2 - \square$
i	0	1			$\frac{1}{2}n^2 - \square$
j		6		10	$\square + \frac{1}{2}n$

___ Exercise 21

1 The table shows the profits made by a company in each of four years.

Year (n)	1	2	3	4
Profit (millions £)	9	13	17	21

a What would you expect the profits to be in the fifth and the sixth years?
b Work out the rule to give the profits in terms of n.
c What would you expect the profits to be in the twentieth year?

2 Look at this pattern of circles:
a Copy and complete the table:

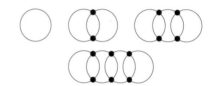

Number of circles (n)	1	2	3	4	5	6
Number of dots	0	2	4			

b Write down the rule to give the number of dots with n circles.
c How many dots would there be in a pattern with 1000 circles?

3 The diagram shows a tower made from identical-sized cubes.
a Copy and complete the table:

Number of layers (n)	1	2	3	4	5	6
Number of cubes in bottom layer	1	5				

b Write down the rule to give the number of cubes, in the bottom layer, of a similar tower n layers high.
c A tower is 20 layers high. How many cubes are there in the bottom layer?

4 A factory produces nails. The table shows the output, in tonnes, in each of four successive months.

Months (n)	1	2	3	4
Output (tonnes)	2.1	4.2	5.3	6.4

a What would you expect the output to be in the fifth and sixth months?   *(Continued)*

b Work out the rule to give the output per month in terms of n.

c What would you expect the output to be in the twentieth month?

5 A rocket is fired into space. The distance it travels, in km, during each of the first four minutes is shown in the table.

Minutes (n)	1	2	3	4
Distance travelled (km)	6.5	8	9.5	11

a How far would you expect the rocket to travel in the fifth and sixth minutes?

b Work out a rule to give the distance travelled during the nth minute.

c During a particular minute in flight, the rocket travelled 20 km. At the end of this minute, for how long had it been travelling since it started?

6 The diagram shows tins stacked in a sequence.

  a Copy and complete the table:

No. of tins on bottom row	1	2	3	4
Total number of tins	1			

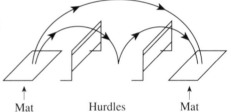

b Write down the rule to give the total number of tins when there are n tins on the bottom row.

c A stack has 20 tins on the bottom row. How many tins are there in the stack?

7 An athlete trains by jumping over low hurdles placed between two mats. The diagram shows the two different ways of crossing with two hurdles.

  a Draw a diagram to show that there are four different ways the athlete can jump over three hurdles.

  b Work out a rule to find the number of different ways the athlete can jump over n hurdles.

  c In theory, there are 512 different ways of jumping over a given number of hurdles. How many hurdles are there?

Mat   Hurdles   Mat

MASTERMINDERS

8 After a meeting of n people, each person shakes hands with each of the others.

  a Write down a rule, in terms of n, to give the total number of handshakes.

  b What would be the minimum number of people at the meeting if more than 5000 handshakes took place?

9 Find the rule to give the sum of the first n counting numbers.

10 The diagram shows a sequence of three squares made with matches. Work out the rule to give the number of matches needed to make the nth square in the sequence.

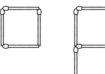
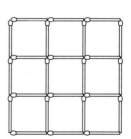

— Revision Exercise 2A

Calculators are **not allowed**.

1 How many metres are there in: **a** 1 km **b** 6 km **c** x km?
2 Find the total cost of: **a** 4 books at £3 each **b** s books at £3 each **c** s books at £t each.
3 Hans is x years old. Write down, in terms of x, Frances's age if she is:
   a 2 years older than Hans.
   b f years older than Hans.
   c t years younger than Hans.
4 Expand and, if possible, simplify: **a** $2(x-3)$ **b** $3(3-e)+2e$ **c** $2e+2(2-e)$ **d** $3r-4(r-2)$
5 When $x = 2$, find the value of: **a** $3x^2$ **b** $(3x)^2$ **c** $(3+x)^2$
6 Solve for x: **a** $3x + 5 = 11$ **b** $5x - 4 = 41$ **c** $\frac{x}{4} - 2 = 4$ **d** $\frac{12}{x} + 7 = 10$
7 The diagram represents a rectangular garden.
   a Find, in terms of x, the perimeter of the garden.
   b If the perimeter is 17 m, write down an equation
   and solve it for x.

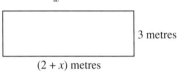

3 metres

$(2 + x)$ metres

8 A rocket is fired into space. It travels seven miles in the first minute, nine miles in the second minute and eleven miles in the third minute. How far would you expect it to travel in **a** the fourth minute **b** the nth minute?

— Revision Exercise 2B

Calculators are **not allowed**.

1 Change the following to metres: **a** 400 cm **b** x cm **c** y km
2 **a** By how much is 19 bigger than x?
   b By how many times is x larger than 17?
   c Find the cost of r records at £y each.
   d n books cost a total of £s. How much does one book cost?
3 Expand and simplify: **a** $5x+5(5+x)$ **b** $6x-6(6-x)$ **c** $7x-(7+x)$ **d** $x+8-8(x+8)+8x$
4 When $x = 4$, find the value of: **a** $(3x)^2$ **b** $(x-3)^2$ **c** $2x^2 + 5x^2$ **d** $2(x^2 + 5x^2)$
5 Solve for x: **a** $2x + 3 = 8$ **b** $20 = 14 - 3x$ **c** $\frac{28}{x} + 19 = 27$ **d** $110 = 100 - \frac{40}{x}$
6 A rocket is fired into space. The distance it travels, in km, during each of the first four minutes is shown in the table.

Minutes (n)	1	2	3	4
Distance travelled (km)	2	5	10	17

How far would you expect it to travel in **a** the fifth minute **b** the nth minute?
7 The smallest of four consecutive odd numbers is $(2k - 3)$.
   a If the sum of the four numbers is n, write an equation connecting k and n.
   b When n is 2000, find each of the four numbers.

Basics Test 2

A Calculator
Solve the following equations:
1 $7x = 133$ 2 $x + 9.84 = 12$ 3 $\frac{x}{9.1} = 1.9$
4 $7.4 = x - 2.85$ 5 $3.95 - x = 1.04$ 6 $21.5 = \frac{4.3}{x}$

B Paper and pencil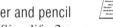
7 Simplify $2 \times a$ 8 Simplify $a \times a$ 9 Simplify $4a + 6a$
10 1.5^2 11 $40.4 - 51.1$ 12 $6.72 \div 7$
13 How many grams are there in x kg?   14 38% of $40\,\text{m}^3$
15 Work out the square root of 256.

C Mental
Ten questions will be read out to you. You need the following facts to answer Questions 16–20.
$a = 4, \quad b = 2, \quad c = \frac{1}{2}$

Puzzler

FIFTEEN Christians and fifteen Turks being at Sea all in one Ship and the same Time in a terrible storm, and the Pilot declaring a necessity of casting the one half of those Persons into the Sea, that the rest might be sav'd, they all agreed, that the Persons to be cast away should be set out by Lot after this manner, that the thirty Persons should be placed in a strait line, and then beginning to count at one of the passengers, and proceeding through the whole, so that every ninth Person should be cast into the Sea, untill of the thirty Persons there remained only Fifteen. The Question is, how those thirty Persons ought to be placed, that the Lot might Infallible fall upon the fifteen Turks, and not upon the fifteen Christians.

Coursework: Straight lines and circles

Figure 1

Figure 1 shows two straight lines intersecting at a single point.

Figure 2 shows three straight lines intersecting at three points and enclosing a single region.

In this Coursework, we are going to see what happens when more lines are drawn and also what happens if we use circles. (In each case we always consider the **maximum** number of points of intersection and the **maximum** number of regions.)

Figure 2

1   Straight lines

a Copy Figure 2. Draw a fourth straight line to intersect at the maximum number of points. Count the total number of points of intersection and the total number of regions enclosed.

b On your diagram draw a fifth line to intersect at the maximum number of points. Count the total number of points and the regions enclosed.

Circles

c Copy Figure 3. With a compass draw a fourth circle to intersect at the maximum number of points. Count the number of points of intersection and the number of regions enclosed.

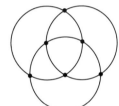

Figure 3

2

Copy the tables below and tabulate your results. Without drawing any more lines or circles, complete the tables. Briefly comment on each of the four series of numbers.

Number of straight lines	Points of intersection	Regions enclosed	Number of circles	Points of intersection	Regions enclosed
2	1	0	2		
3	3	1	3	6	7
4			4		
5			5		
6			6		
7			7		
8			8		
9			9		
10			10		

EXTENSION

3

N			M		
100			100		

3 PROPORTION

3.1 Basic principles

Change of units

REMEMBER

To change from one set of units to another you must either multiply or divide by a certain number. This flow diagram will help you decide what to do.

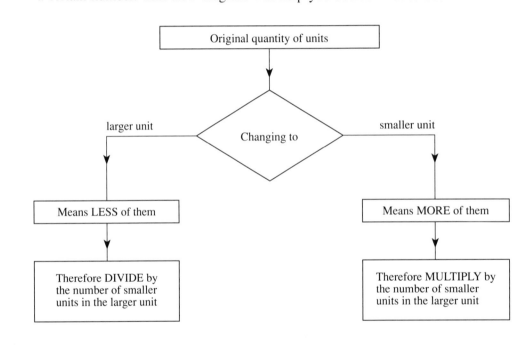

You should be familiar with the following metric conversions:

Length	Mass	Capacity	Area
10 mm = 1 cm	1000 g = 1 kg	1000 ml = 1 litre	100 mm^2 = 1 cm^2
100 cm = 1 m	1000 kg = 1 tonne	1000 cm^3 = 1 litre	10 000 cm^2 = 1 m^2
1000 m = 1 km		1000 litres = 1 m^3	10 000 m^2 = 1 ha*
			100 ha = 1 km^2

* hectare

■ *EXAMPLE 1*

Change $1.2\,m^2$ to cm^2.

(There are $10\,000\,cm^2$ in $1\,m^2$.)

$1.2\,m^2$ is MORE than $1.2\,cm^2$.
Therefore $1.2\,m^2 = 1.2 \times 10\,000\,cm^2$
$= 12\,000\,cm^2$

■ *EXAMPLE 2*

Change 380 seconds to minutes and seconds.

380 seconds is LESS than 380 minutes.

Therefore 380 seconds $= \frac{380}{60} = 6.\dot{3}$ minutes

$= 6\frac{1}{3}$ minutes

$= 6$ minutes 20 seconds

▬ **Problem solving**

The 'Unitary Method' (introduced in Book 1) is a useful means of solving a variety of problems involving two different quantities. Its rules are given here:

> **REMEMBER**
>
> **1** The Question quantity is always put on the lefthand side (LHS).
>
> **2** The Answer quantity is always put on the righthand side (RHS).
>
> **3** If necessary, the Question quantity is changed to unity (one).
>
> **4** All quantities are clearly labelled with their units.
>
> **5** The two quantities are linked using words.

■ *EXAMPLE 3*

A lorry uses 45 litres of diesel to travel 540 km.
a How far would it travel using 1 litre?
b How many litres, to the nearest litre, would the lorry need to travel 175 km?

a

Question quantity   *Answer quantity*

Link with words. — 45 litres is used to go   540 km — We are finding distance, so km quantity is put on RHS.

Therefore 1 litre goes $\frac{540}{45}$ km

Change to unity. — $= 12$ km

b

Question quantity   *Answer quantity*

Link with words. — Lorry travels 540 km on   45 litres — We are finding litres, so litres quantity is put on RHS.

Therefore lorry travels 1 km on $\frac{45}{540}$ litres

Change to unity.

Therefore it travels 175 km on $\frac{45}{540} \times 175$ litres

$= 15$ litres to the nearest litre

Multiply by 175.

49

```
  ┌── REMEMBER
  │       ● Put the Answer quantity on the righthand side.
  │       ● Change the Question quantity to unity (one).
  │
```

■ *EXAMPLE 4*

A landscape architect draws plans of a garden to a scale of 1 : 50.

a   If a garden is 7.5 m wide, find the width of the garden on the plans.

b   If the garden is 25 cm wide on a plan, drawn to a different scale, what is the scale of this plan?

a

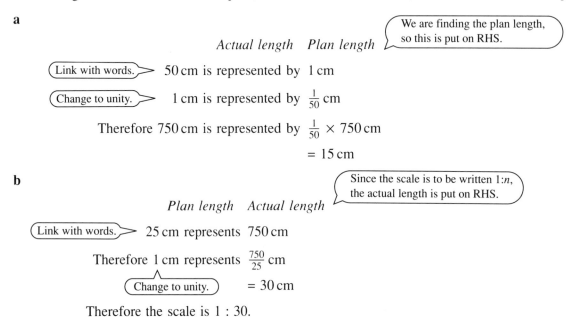

Actual length   Plan length

We are finding the plan length, so this is put on RHS.

Link with words. ⇒ 50 cm is represented by 1 cm

Change to unity. ⇒ 1 cm is represented by $\frac{1}{50}$ cm

Therefore 750 cm is represented by $\frac{1}{50} \times 750$ cm

$$= 15 \text{ cm}$$

b

Since the scale is to be written 1:n, the actual length is put on RHS.

Plan length   Actual length

Link with words. ⇒ 25 cm represents 750 cm

Therefore 1 cm represents $\frac{750}{25}$ cm

Change to unity. $= 30$ cm

Therefore the scale is 1 : 30.

⎯ Exercise 22

1   Thirteen identical books cost £84.50. Find the cost of **a** one book   **b** three books.

2   Over a period of 13 days 1 404 000 people passed through Heathrow Airport. How many would you expect to pass through in **a** 1 day   **b** 365 days?

3   A Tornado fighter aircraft fires 720 bullets in 9 seconds. How many bullets would you expect it to fire in **a** 1 second   **b** 60 seconds?

4   To carpet a room measuring 5 metres by 4 metres costs £610. How much does **a** 1 m² cost **b** 25 m² cost?

5   Seven identical CDs cost £69.93. What is the cost of six CDs?

6  The lift in the Sears Tower in Chicago takes seven seconds to travel 231 feet. The tower is 1454 feet high. Approximately, what would be the least time it would take to reach the top?

7 Throughout the working day in the UK, about 70 000 fax messages are sent every $1\frac{1}{2}$ minutes. Approximately, how many are sent per hour?

8 The bill for four identical meals was £63.60 How much would three meals cost?

9 Which is greater?
    a 3 litres or 2967 ml   **b** 3820 cm or 40 m
    c 6.2 m or 6108 mm   **d** 8200 g or 0.082 tonnes
    e 84.7 mm^2 or 8.4 cm^2 **f** 5600 cm^2 or 5.6 m^2

10 Change to hours and minutes: **a** 525 minutes   **b** 280 minutes   **c** 440 minutes   **d** 174 minutes

11 Change to seconds: **a** $\frac{1}{6}$ of a minute   **b** 0.4 of a minute   **c** 2 hours   **d** $\frac{1}{100}$ of a minute

12 Write each of the following scales in the form $1 : n$, where n is a whole number:
    a 1 cm represents 1 m   **b** 1 cm represents 3 m
    c 1 cm represents 0.4 m   **d** 1 cm represents 0.4 km

13 If the actual length of the cat flea shown is 1.7 mm, work out the scale of the cat flea drawn here.

14 The plans of a house are drawn to a scale of 1 : 50.
    a Find the actual length of a line which is 6 cm long on these plans.
    b If a room is 5.5 m long, find the length, in cm, of the room on these plans.

15 The garden of a house is 25 m long. To draw this on the back of an ordinary envelope, which scale would be the most sensible:
    a 1 : 25
    b 1 : 50
    c 1 : 100
    d 1 : 250
    e 1 : 500?

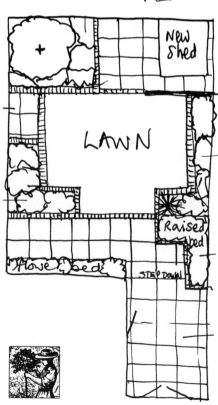

__ 3.2 Change of units

__ Activity 5 ▦

This diagram shows a partially completed car speedometer.

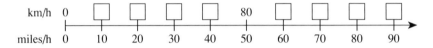

1 Copy the diagram and complete it using a sensible degree of accuracy. Explain:
   a How you worked out your answers.
   b Where you have come across this type of diagram and calculation before.
   c Why the markings on your diagram are not very practical for a speedometer.

2 Now make an exact copy of the diagram but omit the empty boxes on the km/h side. Devise a suitable method to work out the exact values in miles/h of the following speeds:
       20 km/h,   40 km/h,   60 km/h,   100 km/h,   120 km/h,   140 km/h
   a Explain your method.
   b Use your answers to complete the km/h side of your diagram.

3 Look at the diagram and work out an 'easy to remember' approximate conversion for miles to kilometres and vice versa. Use the conversion table on page 53 to compare the accuracy of your answer.

__ Activity 6

The cube represents a cubic centimetre (written cm^3).

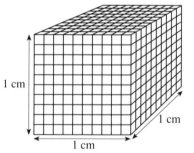

1 cm

1 cm

1 cm

1 Explain how this diagram helps you to understand why there are 1000 cubic millimetres in one cubic centimetre.

2 Draw a similar diagram to represent a cubic metre. Use it to find the number of cubic centimetres in 1 cubic metre.

3 Copy and complete:

| | Unit change | | Operation |
	From	To	
a	cm^3	m^3	
b	cm^3	mm^3	
c	m^3	cm^3	
d	mm^3	cm^3	

— Imperial to metric conversions

'Imperial' is the term used for the British system of units.

Imperial to metric conversions *
1 mile = 1.609 km
1 yard = 0.9144 m
1 inch = 2.540 cm
1 pint = 0.5682 litres
1 pound = 0.4535 kg

* (correct to 4 SF)

Imperial equivalents
1 mile = 1760 yards
1 yard = 3 feet
1 foot = 12 inches
1 gallon = 8 pints
1 pound = 16 ounces

Use these conversions and equivalents in Exercise 23.
Questions about changes of units can be worked out using the 'Unitary Method' (see page 49). Look carefully at the following example.

■ *EXAMPLE 1*

Change 6.4 pints to **a** gallons   **b** litres   **c** cm³.

a

Question quantity	Answer quantity
8 pints	= 1 gallon
1 pint	$= \frac{1}{8}$ gallon
6.4 pints	$= \frac{1}{8} \times 6.4$ gallons
	= 0.8 gallons

b

1 pint is equivalent to   0.5682 litres
6.4 pints are equivalent to 0.5682×6.4 litres
= 3.64 litres to 3 SF

c

1 litre = 1000 cm³
3.64 litres = 3640 cm³

— Exercise 23

Where appropriate, give your answers to 3 SF.

1   Change the following to **a** miles   **b** yards:
(i) 1 km   (ii) 1.8 km   (iii) 1000 m   (iv) 100 m   (v) 483 m

2   Change the following to **a** kg   **b** g:
(i) 1 pound   (ii) 6.4 pounds   (iii) 16 ounces   (iv) 1 ounce   (v) 14 ounces

3   Change the following to **a** pints   **b** gallons:
(i) 1 litre   (ii) 3.4 litres   (iii) 1000 cm³   (iv) 100 cm³   (v) 765 cm³

4   Which is the greater distance, 5000 m or 3 miles?

5   Which is the larger mass: half a pound of butter or 250 g of sugar?

For Questions 6 to 11, select the correct answer from **a**, **b** and **c**.

6 ▦ Potatoes are sold in hundredweight sacks containing 112 pounds of potatoes. This is approximately **a** 50 kg   **b** 100 kg   **c** 220 kg.

7 ▦ A low bridge is 4.2 m high. Paul is driving a bus which is 15 feet 3 inches high. Should he **a** drive under the bridge   **b** not drive under the bridge   **c** proceed with caution?

8 ▦ The bust size of a dress is 34 inches. This is approximately **a** 34 cm   **b** 86 cm   **c** 107 cm.

9 ▦ I need about 4 pints of milk, but the shop sells milk in litres and in half litres. Should I buy **a** 4 litres   **b** $2\frac{1}{2}$ litres   **c** 3 litres?

10 ▦ A car has a 1695 cc ('cc' is another way of writing cm^3) engine. This is approximately **a** 17 litres   **b** 170 litres   **c** 1.7 litres.

11 ▦ A shirt collar has a size of 38 cm. This is approximately **a** 12 inches   **b** 15 inches **c** 18 inches.

MASTERMINDERS

12 ▦ Which is the larger area, a rugby pitch which measures 100 yards by 80 yards or a soccer pitch which is 100 metres square?

13 ▦ Which is the slower speed, 400 miles/h or 643.6 km/h?

___ Activity 7 ▤

You should be able to work out approximate conversions from Imperial to metric (and vice versa), in your head. To help you do this, copy and complete this table and try to memorize the conversions.

Approximate conversions	
Metric to Imperial	*Imperial to metric*
8 km ≈ ☐ miles (1 SF) 1 m ≈ ☐ yards (2 SF) 30 cm ≈ ☐ inches (2 SF) 1 litre ≈ ☐ pints (fraction) 1 kg ≈ ☐ pounds (2 SF)	5 miles ≈ ☐ km (1 SF)

Before attempting Exercise 24, make sure that you know the Imperial equivalents table on page 53.

___ Exercise 24

All these questions may be done mentally. Select the correct answer from **a**, **b** and **c**.

1   One metre is nearest to **a** 1.5 yards   **b** 1.1 yards   **c** 1 yard.

2   One litre is nearest to **a** $1\frac{1}{2}$ pints   **b** $1\frac{1}{4}$ pints   **c** $1\frac{3}{4}$ pints.

3   One kilogram is nearest to **a** 2.2 pounds   **b** 2 pounds   **c** 2.5 pounds.

4 12 kilometres is nearly equal to **a** 8 miles   **b** 6 miles   **c** 5 miles.

5 The number of pints in a gallon is **a** 5   **b** 6   **c** 8.

6 How many yards are there in a mile? **a** 1760   **b** 1670   **c** 1000.

7 The number of inches in 10 cm is nearly equal to **a** 6   **b** 5   **c** 4.

8 A refrigerator weighs 220 pounds. This is approximately **a** 50 kg   **b** 200 kg   **c** 100 kg.

9 To change kilometres to miles you **a** $\times \frac{5}{8}$ **b** $\times \frac{8}{5}$ **c** $\div \frac{5}{8}$.

10 A pin is 1 inch long. This is approximately **a** 24 mm   **b** 2.4 mm   **c** 0.24 cm.

11 100 miles/hour is nearly **a** 50 km/h   **b** 80 km/h   **c** 160 km/h.

MASTERMINDER

12 The number of litres in 1 gallon is approximately **a** 2.5   **b** 5.4   **c** 4.5.

___ **3.3** Exchange rates

Questions about exchange rates can also be worked out using the 'Unitary Method'.
The two examples and each question in Exercise 25 are all based on the exchange rates given below.

Country	Unit of currency	Exchange rate
USA	Dollar ($)	£1 = $1.54
France	Franc (Fr)	£1 = Fr 10.8
Germany	Mark (DM)	£1 = DM 3.06
Spain	Peseta (Ptas)	£1 = Ptas 224

■ *EXAMPLE 1*

How many dollars would you expect to get for £38?

Question quantity   Answer quantity
£1 can be exchanged for $1.54
Therefore £38 can be exchanged for $1.54 × 38 = $58.52

■ *EXAMPLE 2*

How many pounds would you expect to get for Ptas 5600?

Question quantity   Answer quantity
Ptas 224 can be exchanged for £1

Therefore Ptas 1 can be exchanged for £$\frac{1}{224}$

Therefore Ptas 5600 can be exchanged for £$\frac{1}{224}$ × 5600 = £25

55

Exercise 25

1 Change to French francs: **a** £95 **b** £32.50 **c** £78 **d** £12.75.

2 Change to US dollars: **a** £200 **b** £125 **c** £27.50.

3 Change to UK pounds: **a** Ptas 1344 **b** Ptas 5040 **c** Ptas 22 008.

4 Change to UK pounds: **a** DM 459 **b** DM 688.50 **c** DM 596.70 **d** DM 29.07.

5 Which is the odd one out: $11.55, DM 22.95, Fr 78.30 or Ptas 1680?

6 Four families return home from holiday with identical bottles of brandy. The prices paid were: Fr 89.64, $12.32, DM 26.01 and Ptas 1848. Which was the best buy?

7 A man wishes to build a house abroad. He shows the plans to a builder in each of four countries and is given the following prices:

Spain   Ptas 5 292 000
France   Fr 249 750
Germany   DM 71 145
USA $ 36 190

In which country did he get the cheapest offer?

MASTERMINDERS

8 Place the following in order of value, starting with the largest:
Fr 51.3 million
$6.93 million
DM 15.3 million
Ptas 952 million

9 A man saved £3500 for a European holiday. He went first to Germany where he spent DM 3672, second to France where he spent Fr 12 150, and third to Spain where he spent Ptas 260 848. How much money, in £, did he have left if the above figures include his fares?

Activity 8

Investigate some current exchange rates and compare them to those shown on page 55.

3.4 Problem solving

The 'Unitary Method' is a useful way to solve problems involving more than two sets of units.

> *REMEMBER*
>
> - Put the **Answer quantity** on the righthand side
> - Change the **Question quantity** to unity (one).

■*EXAMPLE 1*

On a flight from London to New York, which lasts $3\frac{1}{2}$ hours, Concorde uses 100 800 litres of aviation fuel. (1000 litres = 1 m^3.) Find **a** the fuel consumed per second **b** the time for which the aircraft could fly on 1000 litres of fuel.

a

	Question quantity	*Answer quantity*
In $3\frac{1}{2}$ hours Concorde uses		100 800 litres
In 1 hour Concorde uses		$\frac{100\,800}{3.5}$ litres
In 1 minute Concorde uses		$\frac{100\,800}{60\times3.5}$ litres
In 1 second Concorde uses		$\frac{100\,800}{60\times60\times3.5}$ litres (Do not use your calculator until the last stage)
		$= 8$ litres

b

	Question quantity	*Answer quantity*
100 800 litres are used in		3.5 hours
1 litre is used in		$\frac{3.5}{100\,800}$ hours
1000 litres (1 m^3) are used in		$\frac{3.5\times1000}{100\,800}$ hours
		$= \frac{3500}{100\,800} \times 60 \times 60 = 125$ seconds

Exercise 26

1 The world needle-threading record is 5370 needles in 2 hours. How many needles were completely threaded in **a** 1 hour **b** 1 minute?

2 The world pram-pushing record is 350.23 miles in 24 hours. About how far (to the nearest tenth of a mile) would you expect it to have been pushed in **a** 1 hour **b** 1 minute?

3 In May 1988, a man kissed 4525 women in 8 hours. About how many kisses was he likely to have made in **a** 1 hour **b** 1 minute?

4 The average human loses about a litre of liquid during a 6 hour sleep. About how much is lost (to the nearest 5 cm^3) in **a** 1 hour **b** $\frac{3}{4}$ hour?

5 The UK Government collects, on average, £4.32 million of tax from the sale of alcohol, every 12 hours. How much is collected in **a** 1 hour **b** 1 minute **c** 1 second?

6 The Lord's Prayer, which contains 278 letters, is shown written on an area the size of a postage stamp. This prayer has been written by hand no fewer than 34 times on one side of a stamp measuring 21.33 mm by 18.03 mm. How many completed letters were written per mm^2? How many letters can you write in a square centimetre?

7 To pass a typing exam a candidate must type 40 words per minute. If someone typed 525 words in $12\frac{1}{2}$ minutes, would they pass the exam?

8 **Investigate** these figures:

Tinned fruit
450 g tin costs 99p
420 g tin costs 87p
310 g tin costs 69p

9 The price of gold is £25 per gram. The largest size of gold bar has a mass of 11.8 kg.
a What is the cost of one bar?
b What mass of gold is worth £1?

10 Ketna makes an apple pie for six people and uses $1\frac{1}{2}$ pounds of apples.
a How many pounds of apples should she use in a pie for seven people?
b How many people is the pie for if she uses $3\frac{1}{2}$ pounds of apples?

11 The height of the world's tallest free-standing structure, the CN Tower in Toronto, is 1122 feet. (See photograph.) The stair-climbing record to the top is 8 minutes 28 seconds.
a How high would you expect the record-holder to climb per second?
b How long would you expect the record-holder to take to climb 100 feet?

12 A car travels 350 km and uses 56 litres of petrol.

a How far would you expect it to travel using 32 litres?

b How many litres would you expect it to use over a distance of 112.5 km?

13 **Investigate** these figures:

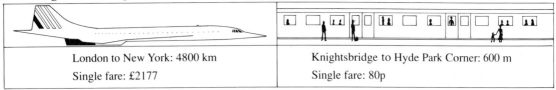

| London to New York: 4800 km | Knightsbridge to Hyde Park Corner: 600 m |
| Single fare: £2177 | Single fare: 80p |

14 While hovering, a Harrier 'jump jet' uses about 200 pounds of fuel per minute. Assuming that 1 gallon of fuel has a mass of about 8 pounds, find **a** how long it takes to use 1 gallon of fuel **b** the number of pints of fuel it uses per second.

15 The scale of a map is 1 : 50 000.

a If two towns on the map are shown 4 cm apart, find their actual distance apart in km.

b A straight road is 2.5 km long. Find the length of this road on the map in cm.

16 The scale of a map is 1 : 25 000. Find the distance between two points on the map in mm if on the land they are **a** 1 km **b** 5 km **c** 250 m apart.

17 **Investigate** why nearly all models made from kits **used** to be made to the scale of 1 : 72.

18 **Investigate** how high a human appears to an ant.

MASTERMINDERS

19 Find, to 2 SF, the mpg (miles per gallon) of a car which travels **a** 289 miles using 42 litres **b** 247 km using 8 gallons **c** 467 km using 74 litres.

20 Concorde takes $2\frac{1}{2}$ hours to fly 3600 km and uses a mean of 8 litres of fuel per second. The QE2 sails at an average speed of 36 km/h and uses a mean of 10 litres of fuel per second.

a How far will each travel, to the nearest kilometre, using 1 litre of fuel?

b How far will each travel, to the nearest yard, using 1 gallon of fuel?

c Show that: m/litre × 5 ≈ yards/gallon

21 The density of aviation fuel is about 0.8 g/cm³. Show that the mass of a gallon of fuel is about 8 pounds. What do you think the mass of a gallon of water is?

___ 3.5 Science problems

___ Activity 9 ▦

Four pieces of different metals are taken, and their volumes and masses are measured. The results, correct to 3 SF, are shown below.

Metal	Mass (g)	Volume (cm³)
Aluminium	40.2	14.9
Brass	122	14.3
Gold	281	14.8
Platinum	317	15.1

1 For each metal work out, to 2 SF, the mass per cm^3 and put your results in a table.

You have worked out the 'density' of the metal, that is, the ratio of mass to volume.

___ REMEMBER

Density (g/cm³) = Mass, in g, of 1 cm³

2 Copy and complete:

Substance	Mass (g)	Volume (cm³)	Density (g/cm³)
	135	50	
	459	54	
		10	21
			1
Oak	46.2	55	
Petrol	46.8		0.72
Air	1200		0.0012
	M	V	

a Write down the answer to the last line as an equation.
b Work out the approximate mass of the air in your classroom.
c **Investigate** whether you would be able to lift a pin head, if it were made from a neutron star.
   (The density of a neutron star is about 500 000 000 tonnes/cm³.)

Exercise 27

1 ▦ A piece of wire is 2 m long and has a resistance of 5 ohms.
   a What would be the resistance of a piece of wire 5 m long?
   b What length of wire would have a resistance of 17.5 ohms?

2 ▦ 100 g of sugar is converted by the body into 1650 kJ (kilojoules) of energy.
   a How much energy would you be able to get from 750 g of sugar?
   b How much sugar can be converted into 660 kJ of energy?

3 ▦ When 1.5 g of peanut is burnt, 36 kJ of energy are released.
   a How much energy is released if 20 g is burnt?
   b What mass of peanut would have to be burnt to release 108 kJ of energy?

4 ▦ 100 g of brown bread contains 2.5 mg (milligrams) of iron. How much brown bread would you need to eat to obtain your daily requirement of 14 mg, if brown bread were your only food?

5 ▦ The energy content of food used to be measured in calories. Today we measure energy in joules, where 4.2 kJ = 1 kcalorie. Copy and complete the following table:

   If someone has a meal consisting of 200 g of potatoes, 500 g of bread, 500 g of chicken and 100 g of beans, what is the total energy content of the meal in **a** kJ **b** kcal?

Food	Energy per 100 g	
	kcal	*kJ*
Potatoes, boiled	79	
Bread, white	253	
Chicken, roast	184	
Beans	92	

6 ▦ **a** Explain why the scale of 250 : 1 is another way of writing a magnification of ×250.
   b Look carefully at the three diagrams. By taking suitable measurements, copy and complete the table.

	White blood cell	Sperm	Cell from a green leaf
Scale	3000:1		
Magnification		× 1500	
Actual	Width = . . . mm	Length = . . . mm	Length = 0.2 mm

MASTERMINDER

7 ▦ **Investigate** the following: each minute your heart beats about 75 times and pumps about 5 litres of blood around your body.

3 PROPORTION

___ Revision Exercise 3A

Calculators are allowed.

1 Change **a** 200 minutes to hours and minutes **b** a third of an hour to minutes.
2 Change **a** 240 mm^3 to cm^3 **b** 24 pints to gallons.
3 Given that 1 yard ≈ 0.91 m, select the most accurate conversion:
  a 25 yards is approximately: 23 m, 25 m, 27 m.
  b 60 m is approximately: 54 yards, 60 yards, 66 yards.
4 Given an exchange rate of Fr 3 = DM 1, change **a** DM 6.9 to francs **b** Fr 420 to marks.
5 Five identical CDs cost £52. What is the cost of **a** 1 CD **b** 3 CDs?
6 If the can of sweetcorn costs £1.25, find the cost, in pence, of
  a 1 g **b** 40 g.

7 A car travels 160 miles and uses 5 gallons of petrol.
  a How far would you expect it to have travelled if it used 11 gallons?
  b How many gallons would you expect it to use in travelling 416 miles?
8 A lump of brass has a mass of 189 g and a volume of 21 cm^3.
  a Find the mass of a 50 cm^3 lump.
  b Write down the density of brass in the form, 'g/cm^3'.

___ Revision Exercise 3B

Calculators are allowed.

1 Change **a** 232 minutes to hours and minutes **b** 0.4 hours to minutes.
2 Change **a** 0.006 m^3 to cm^3 **b** 2800 cm^3 to litres.
3 Given that 1 mile = 1760 yards ≈ 1.6 km, work out the following conversions.
  a 1 metre ≈ ... yards
  b 1 km ≈ ... miles.
4 Given £1 = $1.8 and £1 = Fr 10.8, change **a** £15 to francs **b** $360 to pounds **c** $26 to francs.
5 On an eight-hour flight an aircraft uses 1200 litres of fuel. **a** Find how long it takes to use
  9.5 litres. **b** Write down the fuel consumption in litres/minute.
6 Which is the best buy?

'PURR' tinned cat food
320 g tin costs 36 p
400 g tin costs 46 p
470 g tin costs 52 p

7 The scale of a map is 1 : 25 000.
  a If two villages on the map are shown 5 cm apart, find their actual distance apart in km.
  b A straight road is 3.5 km long. Find, in cm, the length of this road on the map.
8 The cuboid of material shown here has a density of 8.4 g/cm^3.
  If its mass is 80.64 g, find the value of x.

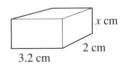

Basics Test 3

A Calculator
Work out each answer correct to 1 DP.

1 $\frac{39.1}{28 \times 1.09}$ **2** What is $67\frac{1}{2}\%$ of 99 miles?

3 Change 0.0814 hours to minutes.   **4** $\frac{39.1}{28} \div 1.09$

5 $\frac{39.1}{28} \div (1.09)^2$ **6** Change $\frac{59}{73}$ to a percentage.

B Paper and pencil

7 Simplify $c + c$ **8** Simplify $c \times c$ **9** $\frac{2}{3} + \frac{3}{4}$

10 $\frac{2}{3} \div \frac{3}{4}$ **11** 38.7×0.8 **12** $101.4 \div 13$

13 Estimate the square root of 200.

14 Solve for a: $12.9 + a = 304.1$.

15 Approximately, how many miles are there in 40 km?

C Mental
Ten questions will be read out to you.

At a certain time, the exchange rate between the Spanish peseta and British pound was Ptas 223 to £1. The following shows several approximate conversions of this exchange rate. Use these approximations to answer Questions 16 to 20.

£1 ≈ Ptas 225   10p ≈ Ptas 22.5   Ptas 900 ≈ £4
£4 ≈ Ptas 900   1p ≈ Ptas 2.25   Ptas 90 ≈ 40p

Puzzlers

1 The sum of three consecutive numbers is 291. Find the numbers.

2 After a committee meeting, every member shook hands with every other member. If there were 28 hand shakes altogether, how many were on the committee?

3 Work out the ratio of the respective areas of the two shapes drawn in the diagram.

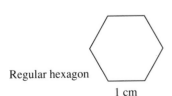
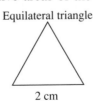

Equilateral triangle

Regular hexagon

1 cm   2 cm

4 What is the maximum number of points of intersection of five circles and ten straight lines? (You may find the Coursework on page 47 helpful.)

Coursework: The Humber Bridge

In this Coursework you are going to make a scale model of the main span of the Humber Bridge (the longest suspended span in the world); and also a scale drawing of the whole bridge.

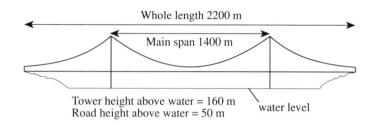

Whole length 2200 m
Main span 1400 m
Tower height above water = 160 m
Road height above water = 50 m
water level

1 Scale model

a Copy the table below and use a scale of 1 : 250 to complete it.

Actual	Model		Actual	Model
250 m	1 m		1000 m	m
1 m	mm		50 m	cm
160 m	cm		1400 m	m

b Use your scaled dimensions to make a model of the main span of the bridge out of two laboratory stools and a thick piece of rope as shown below. (You may have to increase the height of each stool.)

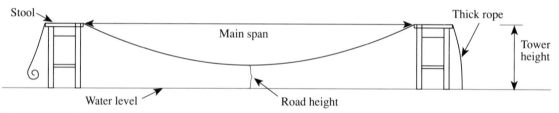

Stool
Main span
Thick rope
Tower height
Water level
Road height

c Make a cardboard cut-out of Nelson's Column to the same scale and place it by your model. (Nelson's Column is about 60 m high.)

2 Scale drawing

a Copy and complete the following table:

Scale	Length of bridge		Scale	Length of bridge
1 : 100	m		1 : 500	m
1 : 1000	m		1 : 2500	cm
1 : 5000	cm		1 : 10 000	cm
1 : 25 000	cm		1 : 50 000	cm

b Choose the most suitable scale to make a scale drawing of the whole bridge. Make a scale drawing of other objects to illustrate the size of the bridge.

EXTENSION

3 Investigate the following facts about the two suspension cables:

There are 14 948 individual wires in each cable. The total volume of both cables is about 6000 m^3. The density of the wire is about 8 g/cm^3.

4 GEOMETRY I

4.1 Basic principles

Angle properties

1 Angles vertically opposite

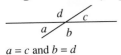

$a = c$ and $b = d$

2 Angles on a straight line

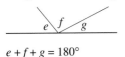

$e + f + g = 180°$

3 Angles at a point

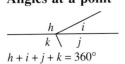

$h + i + j + k = 360°$

> **REMEMBER**
> - Vertically opposite angles are equal.
> - The angles on a straight line (adjacent angles) add up to 180°.
> - The sum of the angles at a point is 360°.

■ *EXAMPLE 1*

Find angle y, giving the reason.

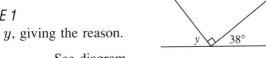

[F]   See diagram
[E] and [S] $38° + 90° + y = 180°$ (Angles on a straight line)
[W] $128° + y = 180°$
             $y = 180° - 128° = 52°$ ⟨Reason⟩

■ *EXAMPLE 2*

Giving reasons, find:
a The value of n.
b The size of angle AOC.
c The size of angle AOD.

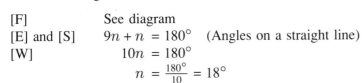

a [F]   See diagram
    [E] and [S] $9n + n = 180°$ (Angles on a straight line)
    [W] $10n = 180°$
                 $n = \frac{180°}{10} = 18°$

b $A\hat{O}C = 18°$ (Vertically opposite)

c $A\hat{O}D = C\hat{O}B$ (Vertically opposite)
       $= 9 \times 18° = 162°$

65

— Triangle properties

(Lines of symmetry are shown as broken lines on the diagrams.)

Equilateral triangle
- 3 equal sides
- 3 equal angles
- 3 lines of symmetry

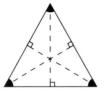

Isosceles triangle
- 2 equal sides
- 2 equal angles
- 1 line of symmetry

Triangle ABC is **right-angled isosceles**.
(One angle is 90°.)

Triangle DEF is **acute-angled isosceles**.
(All angles are less than 90°.)

Triangle GHI is **obtuse-angled isosceles**.
(One angle is more than 90°.)

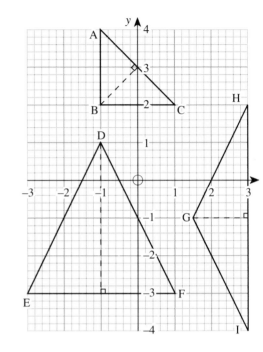

The three corners (called the **vertices**) of each triangle are identified by the co-ordinates:

A (-1, 4), B (-1, 2), C (1, 2)
D (-1, 1), E (-3, -3), F (1, -3)
G ($1\frac{1}{2}$, -1), H (3, 2), I (3, -4)

A 'scalene' triangle has no axes of symmetry and therefore has no equal angles or equal sides. It can be right-angled.

REMEMBER

The angle sum of a triangle is 180°.

■ *EXAMPLE 3*
Find the unknown angles, giving reasons.

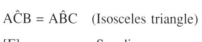

$\hat{ACB} = \hat{ABC}$ (Isosceles triangle)

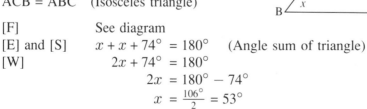

[F]   See diagram
[E] and [S] $x + x + 74° = 180°$ (Angle sum of triangle)
[W] $2x + 74° = 180°$
                    $2x = 180° - 74°$
                    $x = \frac{106°}{2} = 53°$

[E] and [S] $53° + y = 180°$ (Angles on a straight line)
[W] $y = 180° - 53° = 127°$

66

___ Exercise 28

For Questions 1 and 2, draw axes for x and y from 4 to -4, using the same scale on both axes.

1 Plot the points: A $(1, -1)$, B $(-2, -4)$, C $(4, -4)$, D $(1, 0)$, E $(4, 0)$, F $(2\frac{1}{2}, 4)$, G $(-1, -1)$, H $(-4, -1)$, I $(-4, 2)$.
Draw triangles ABC, DEF and GHI. For each triangle, draw any lines of symmetry and name the type of triangle.

2 Plot the points: L $(4, -1\frac{1}{2})$, M $(4, -3)$, N $(1\frac{1}{2}, -3)$, O $(2, 2)$, P $(3, 1)$, Q $(2, 4)$, R $(-4, 3)$, S $(-\frac{1}{2}, 1)$, T $(-4, -1)$.
Draw triangles LMN, OPQ and RST. For each triangle, draw any lines of symmetry and name the type of triangle.

For Questions 3 to 18, find the unknown angles, giving reasons.

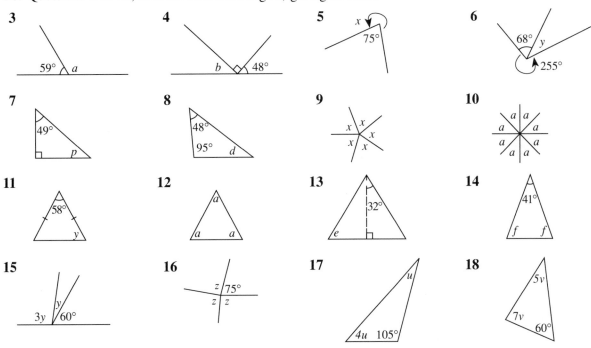

For Questions 19 and 20, explain why each of the triangles must be isosceles.

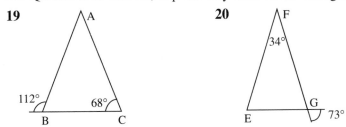

21 a Explain how the diagram in Question 9 could be made into a **regular** pentagon.
b Make a neat drawing of (i) a regular ten-sided figure (ii) a regular twelve-sided figure.

22 The six figures (i) to (vi) are drawn so that each can have a line of symmetry.

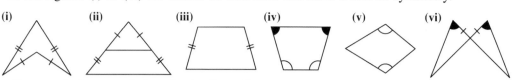

(i)   (ii)   (iii)   (iv)   (v)   (vi)

a Copy each figure and draw in the line of symmetry.

b Which figures can be drawn, **using only the facts shown**, in such a way that they do **not have** a line of symmetry? Draw separate diagrams to illustrate your answers.

___ 4.2 Parallel lines

Parallel lines are always the same distance apart. In order to show that lines are parallel, an arrowhead is placed on each line, as shown in this diagram.

A line which crosses parallel lines is called a **transversal**.

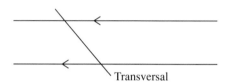

Transversal

___ *Activity 10*

Using the sides of your ruler, draw two parallel lines. Also draw a transversal and label the angles as shown.

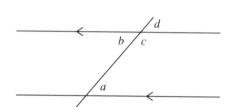

1   Alternate angles
Show by measuring that $a = b$. These angles are equal because they are in an 'alternate' position.

2   Corresponding angles
$b = d$ (Vertically opposite)
$b = a$ (Alternate angles)
Therefore $a = d$
Angles a and d are equal because they are in a 'corresponding' position.

3   Allied angles
$b + c = 180°$ (Angles on a straight line)
$b = a$ (Alternate angles)
Therefore $a + c = 180°$
The sum of angles a and c equals $180°$ because the angles are in an 'allied' position.
(*Continued*)

REMEMBER

- Alternate angles a and b are equal.

- Corresponding angles a and d are equal.

- Allied angles a and c add up to $180°$.

4 Comment on the following diagrams:

a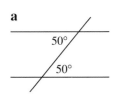

b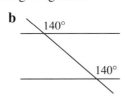

c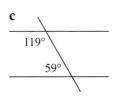

d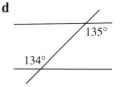

■ *EXAMPLE 1*

Find the lettered angles, giving reasons.

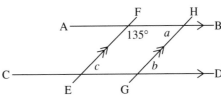

[F]   See diagram

[E] and [S] $a + 135° = 180°$ (Allied angles, EF is parallel to GH)

[W] $a = 180° - 135° = 45°$

$b = a$ (Alternate angles, AB is parallel to CD)

Therefore $b = 45°$

$c = b$ (Corresponding angles, EF is parallel to GH)

Therefore $c = 45°$

(Notice that in diagrams with more than one set of parallel lines, the appropriate lines have to be named in the reason.)

▬ Exercise 29

1 State whether each of the following pairs of angles are alternate, corresponding, allied, adjacent or vertically opposite. State also whether they are equal, or total 180°.

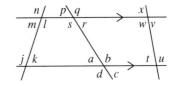

a k and m	**b** k and l	**c** k and j
d b and s	**e** b and q	**f** b and r
g b and a	**h** b and d	**i** r and c
j r and q	**k** r and p	**l** v and u
m v and x	**n** l and j	**o** t and w

For Questions 2 to 5, find the lettered angles, giving reasons.

2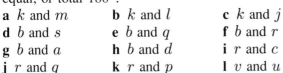

3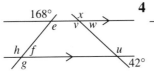

4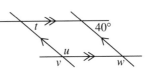

5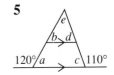

For Questions 6 to 10, find the lettered angles, giving reasons.

6 Explain why WX is parallel to YZ.

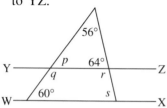

7

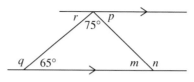

8

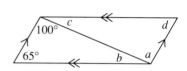

9

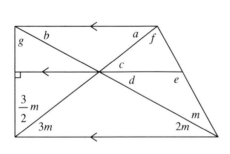

10 Explain why AD is parallel to BC and why AB is parallel to DC.

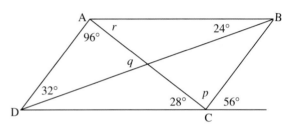

MASTERMINDERS

For Questions 11 and 12, find the lettered angles, giving reasons.

11

12

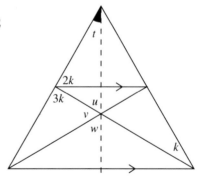

__ 4.3 Symmetry of quadrilaterals

__ *Activity 11*

1   Take a piece of paper and fold it in half. Take a pair of scissors. Into the fold and **using only two cuts**, try to cut out:

a An arrowhead.   b An acute-angled kite.

c An obtuse-angled kite.   d A right-angled kite.

Your result should resemble the diagrams below.

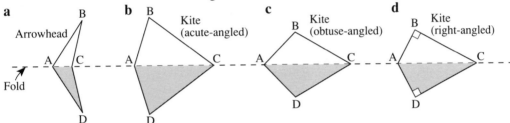

(The fold is the line of symmetry of each quadrilateral.)

Stick each of the four quadrilaterals into your book by putting glue **only on the shaded parts shown**. Label each with its correct name. Fold each quadrilateral along its line of symmetry to demonstrate the following:

$AB = AD$, $DC = BC$, $A\hat{B}C = A\hat{D}C$, $A\hat{C}B = A\hat{C}D$, $C\hat{A}B = C\hat{A}D$

2   Take four pieces of paper and fold each one in half along two separate directions at right angles to one another, in order to find the middle. Starting at the middle, with your paper folded, make the following cut-outs:

a A square, by making **one cut only**.   b A rhombus by making **one cut only**.

c A square by making **two cuts**.   d A rectangle by making **two cuts**.

Your results should resemble the diagrams below: Stick these into your book by putting glue **only on the shaded parts**. Label each with its correct name. (*Continues on next page.*)

a Square   b Rhombus   c Square   d Rectangle

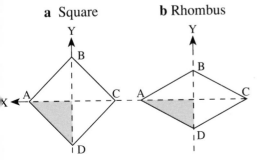
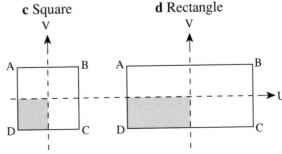

The properties of these quadrilaterals can also be deduced by symmetry. For example, if we fold the rhombus along the axis Y, the following facts are true:

BC = AB, DC = AD, BĈD = BÂD

These properties are shown on this table. Copy and complete the table. Leave a blank space for each case where the statement is either false or not **directly** true because of the line of symmetry.

Statement	Square	Rhombus	Rectangle
AB = BC		Y	
AB = AD			
AB = CD			
BC = AD			
BC = DC			
AD = CD		Y	

Statement	Square	Rhombus	Rectangle
AB̂C = AD̂C			
AB̂C = BD̂C			
AB̂C = BÂD			
AD̂C = BĈD			
AD̂C = BÂD			
BÂD = BĈD		Y	

3   Draw accurately each of the four quadrilaterals shown here.

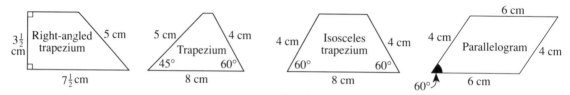

By measuring the angles which are not given, deduce the properties of each quadrilateral.

■ *EXAMPLE 1*

Find the lettered angles, giving reasons.

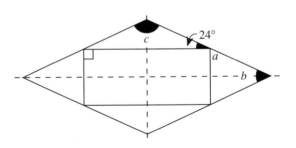

[F]   See diagram

[E] and [S] $24° + 90° + a = 180°$ (Angles on a straight line)
[W]   Therefore $a = 66°$

[E] and [S] $66° + 66° + b = 180°$ (Angle sum of triangle)
[W]   Therefore $b = 48°$

[E] and [S] $48° + c = 180°$ (Allied angles)
[W]   Therefore $c = 132°$

__ Exercise 30

For Questions 1 to 3, name the type(s) of included quadrilateral, writing down the vertices in each case.

1
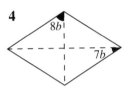

2
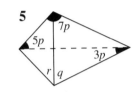

3
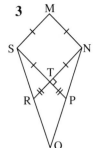

For Questions 4 to 9, find the lettered angles, giving reasons.

4
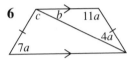

5

6
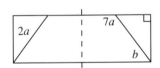

7

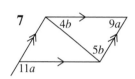

MASTERMINDERS

8
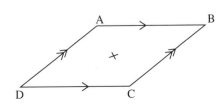

9

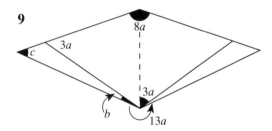

__ 4.4 Rotational symmetry

Some shapes fit into the same position more than once when rotated through 360°. When this happens the shape is said to have 'rotational symmetry'.

For example, this figure has rotational symmetry order 3. Can you see why?

A parallelogram has rotational symmetry order 2. This fact about its symmetry tells us that AD = BC, $A\hat{B}C = A\hat{D}C$, $D\hat{A}B = D\hat{C}B$, AB = DC.

73

Exercise 31

1 Make separate neat drawings of each type of quadrilateral which has rotational symmetry order 2 or 4. Name the quadrilateral and its order of symmetry. In each case list the properties which can be deduced **because of** the order of symmetry.

2 Name a triangle which has rotational symmetry. What is its order?

3 This figure is a regular pentagon ABCDE with centre O.
   a Explain why (i) you think it is called 'regular'
   (ii) it has rotational symmetry order 5.
   b What do you notice about OA, OB, OC, OD and OE?

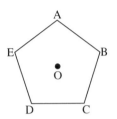

4 A regular figure has n sides. What is its order of symmetry?

4.5 Angles of a polygon

Activity 12

Copy the three diagrams and the table below. Use the diagrams to complete the table.

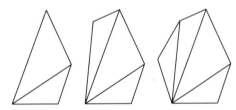

Number of sides of figure	Number of triangles in figure	Angle sum of figure
4	2	$2 \times 180° = 360°$
5	3	=
6		=
n		=

Show that your last answer can be simplified to give $90(2n - 4)°$. It is easier to remember this formula if you replace $90°$ with 'right angles'.

> **REMEMBER**
>
> Angle sum of an n-sided figure
> $= (2n - 4)$ right angles

If the polygon is 'regular', then all the interior angles are equal.

> **REMEMBER**
>
> Each interior angle of a regular n-sided
> polygon $= \dfrac{(2n-4)\ \text{right angles}}{n}$

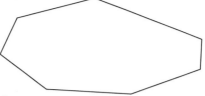

■ EXAMPLE 1

Find the angle sum of this figure:

[F]	$n = 7$
[E]	Angle sum $= (2n - 4)$ right angles
[S]	$= (2 \times 7 - 4)90$
[W]	$= 900°$

■ EXAMPLE 2

If the polygon in Example 1 were regular, find each interior angle.

[F] $n = 7$

[E]   Each angle $= \dfrac{(2n - 4) \text{ right angles}}{n}$

[S] $= \dfrac{(2 \times 7 - 4)90}{7}$

[W] $= \dfrac{900}{7} = 129°$ (correct to the nearest degree)

—— Exercise 32

1 Find the angle sum of: **a** an eight-sided figure   **b** a ten-sided figure   **c** a 200-sided figure.

2 Find the value of each interior angle of a regular figure with **a** 8 sides   **b** 20 sides
   c 200 sides.

3 Angles a, b, c, d and e are called 'exterior angles'.
   a Show that $a + b + c + d + e = 360°$.
   b Find the sum of the exterior angles of a ten-sided
      figure. Comment on your result.

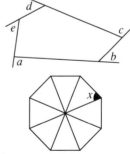

4 This figure is a regular octagon. Find the value of
   x by using two different methods.

5 A polygon has an angle sum of $1620°$. Find the number of sides.

6 Find the number of sides in the polygons whose angle sum is **a** $1260°$ **b** $2520°$ **c** $9000°$.

7 This hexagon is divided into six triangles. Use these
   triangles to show that the angle sum of the hexagon
   is $720°$.

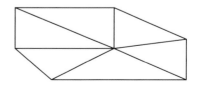

MASTERMINDERS

8 Which of the following angles can be the interior angle of a regular polygon: 160°, 161°, 162°, 163°, 164°, 165°?

9 How many regular polygons have interior angles between 170° and 171°?

10 The angles of a pentagon are in the ratio 2 : 3 : 4 : 4 : 5. Find the angles. What must be the order of the angles to make two sides parallel?

11 Show that the exterior angle of a regular n-sided polygon equals 360° ÷ n.

12 The interior angles of a regular polygon are each 140°. What is the size of an interior angle of a regular polygon with three more sides than the original polygon?

13 A regular octagon has vertices (corners) A, B, C, D, E, F, G, H. Join AE, AF, and AG. Work out all the angles in the figure.

▬ 4.6 Miscellaneous calculations

▬ Exercise 33

1

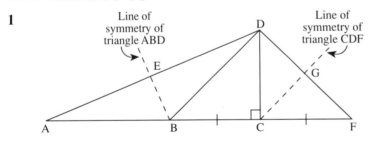

Which of the following **must** be true?
a AB = BD   **b** CD = CF   **c** BD = FD   **d** BD = ED
e BÊD = 90°   **f** BÂE = BD̂E   **g** CD̂F = 45°   **h** GĈD = 45°
i CB̂D = CF̂D   **j** CB̂D = FĈG

For Questions 2 to 5, find the lettered angles, giving reasons.

2   **3**   **4**   **5**

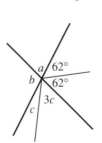   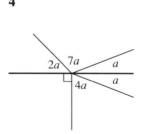   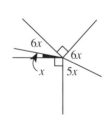

For Questions 6 to 11, find the lettered angles, giving reasons.

6 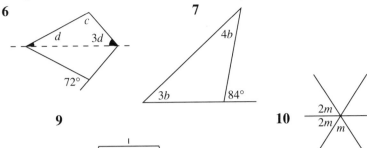 **7**

8

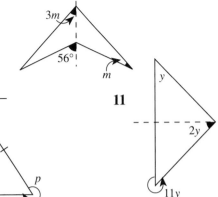

9

10 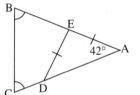 **11**

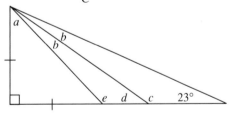

12 Through how many degrees does the minute hand of a clock turn during:
   a 60 minutes   **b** 40 minutes   **c** 35 minutes?

13 Through how many degrees does the hour hand of a clock turn during:
   a 1 hour   **b** $\frac{1}{2}$ hour   **c** $7\frac{1}{2}$ hours   **d** $3\frac{1}{2}$ hours?

14 How long does it take (i) the minute hand   (ii) the hour hand of a clock to turn through:
   a 60°   **b** 120°   **c** 150°   **d** 270°
   e 300°   **f** 75°   **g** 315°   **h** 165°?

15 Find each of the following angles:
   a AĈB   **b** AD̂E   **c** AÊD   **d** DÊB   **e** ED̂C
   Find the value of DÊB + EB̂C + BĈD + CD̂E.

16 Find the lettered angles, giving reasons.

MASTERMINDERS

17 In the figure, AB = BC = CD = DE = EF = FG.
   a Write all the other angles in terms of x.
   b Find the value of each angle if $x = 12°$.
   c Find the value of x if
      (i) GF̂X = 90° (ii) EF̂G = 90°.

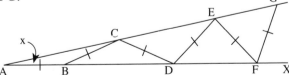

18 Find the angle between the hands of a clock at the following times:
   a 01:12   **b** 01:24   **c** 13:36   **d** 03:36   **e** 09:12
   f 21:24   **g** 02:24   **h** 14:48   **i** 05:12

▬ Revision Exercise 4A

Calculators are **not allowed**.

In Questions 1 and 2, find the lettered angles, giving reasons.

1 Name the type of triangle shown.

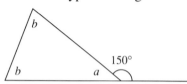

2 Name the type of quadrilateral shown.

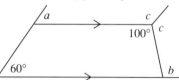

3 The line MN is the line of symmetry of the figure ABCD.
Copy and complete: **a** AD = ...
b DÂB = ... **c** MB = ... **d** CN̂M = ...°
e ABCD is called ... **f** AB is ... to DC.

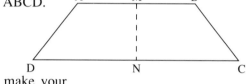

4 Make a large copy of this figure. (Do not try to make your
drawing exactly the same shape as this one.)
a Use your drawing to help explain why the angle sum of a
six-sided figure is 720°.
b Comment on the sides, angles and rotational symmetry of a
regular six-sided figure.

▬ Revision Exercise 4B

Calculators are **not allowed**.

In Questions 1 and 2, find the lettered angles, giving reasons.

1 Explain why AB is parallel to DC.

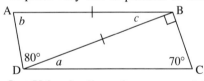

2

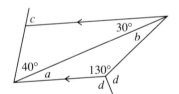

3 Let X be the line of symmetry AC.
Let Y be the line of symmetry BD.
Let Z be the rotational symmetry order 2.
Indicate the reason, X, Y or Z, why each of the
following statements is true. For example,
AB = BC because of Y.
a AB = AD **b** AB = CD **c** AB̂D = CB̂D
d BĈA = CÂD **e** BO = OD **f** BĈA = BÂC.

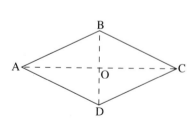

4 Find the angle sum of a nine-sided figure.
5 Find the value of each interior angle of a regular ten-sided figure.
6 The interior angles of a regular polygon are each 150°. How many sides does it have?

Basics Test 4

A Calculator

1 Solve for x: $6.81 + x = 9.4$

2 Solve for y: $0.38 = 2 - y$

3 $\frac{3.2+9.82}{13}$ to 2 SF

4 $\frac{13}{3.2+9.82}$ to 2 SF

5 Solve for s: $27 = \frac{s}{0.8}$

6 Solve for t: $\frac{2.21}{t} = 13$

B Paper and pencil

7 When $x = 2$, $4x^2 = ?$

8 When $y = -3$, $y^2 - y = ?$

9 Simplify: $2a(2a - 5)$

10 Change $380\,mm^2$ to cm^2.

11 $1\frac{2}{3} \div \frac{1}{5}$

12 $(0.13)^2$

13 What is 8% of £55?

14 If $89 \times 98 = 8722$, $\frac{8722}{9.8} = ?$

15 $(78 \times 0.479) \div 0.0781$ is nearest to which of the following: 50, 500, 5000?

C Mental

Ten questions will be read out to you. Use the following facts to answer Questions 16 to 20.

Cost of local telephone calls

Charge rate period	Call duration				
	1 min	2 min	3 min	4 min	5 min
Cheap rate	5p	5p	5p	5p	5p
Standard rate	5p	10p	10p	15p	20p
Peak rate	5p	10p	15p	20p	25p

Puzzlers

1 A man was x years old in AD x^2. How old was he in 1987? (x is a whole number.)

2 Find the next five numbers in the sequence: 1, 2, 3, 3, 3, 6, 5, 4, 9, 7, 5 ...

3 From a piece of paper, cut out a square and lightly shade it one side of it with a coloured pencil. Mark in the lines shown. Cut along each dotted line. Now fold your square to make a cube with all its six outside faces coloured.

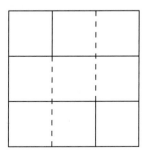

Coursework: Parallel lines

This Coursework explores ways of using parallel lines to make various constructions. The parallel lines are drawn using only the two edges of a ruler and **the markings on the ruler may not be used at any time**.

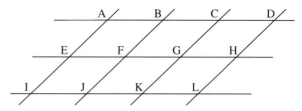

Figure 1

1 Copy Figure 1. **Investigate** the different types of quadrilateral included within ADLI. Draw separate diagrams to illustrate your findings.

2 Construct a rhombus. Draw in the diagonals. Mark all the equal angles and equal lines. Comment on its symmetrical properties.

3 Figure 2 shows the stages involved in bisecting (dividing into two equal halves) the line XY.

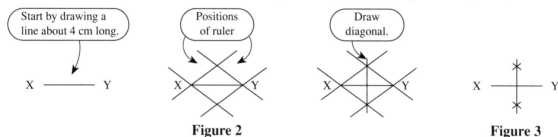

Figure 2   **Figure 3**

However, it is better to reduce the construction lines to the length shown in Figure 3. Use this method to construct the following.
a The perpendicular bisector of a given straight line (the line which divides it into two equal parts at right angles).
b The bisector of a given angle.
c A right angle.
d A square.

EXTENSION

4 **a** Draw a line AB about 12 cm long and on it mark a point P, but not in the middle.

Construct the perpendicular to AB . through P.

b Draw a line AB about 12 cm long and a point P, not on the line and not in the middle.

•P

A ———————————————— B

Construct the perpendicular to AB from the point P.

5 GRAPHS I

5.1 Basic principles

A graph can be drawn to illustrate a relationship between two quantities. The Activity below investigates, on one graph, four different exchange rates between the US dollar and the UK pound.

Activity 13

On graph paper, draw a horizontal axis to represent UK pounds from £0 to £50, by using a scale of 2 cm to £10. Draw a vertical axis to represent US dollars from $0 to $120, by using a scale of 2 cm to $20.

1   Write down the scale of:
    a The horizontal axis in the form, '2 mm represents £...'.
    b The vertical axis in the form, '2 mm represents $...'.

2   Carefully plot, with a cross, each of the following co-ordinates onto your graph:
    (10, 15), (10, 19), (10, 28), (10, 40), (20, 30), (20, 38), (20, 56), (20, 80),
    (30, 45), (30, 84), (30, 120), (40, 60), (40, 76), (40, 112), (50, 75), (50, 95).
    Each of the points should lie on one of four straight lines. Draw these four lines and, starting with the top one, label them A, B, C and D.

3   The lines A, B, C and D represent the exchange rates in 1947, 1967, 1977 and 1987 respectively. Copy and complete the table. Explain why all four lines could meet at one point on your graph.

Date	Exchange rate
1947	£1 = $ ...
1967	£1 = $ ...
1977	£1 = $ ...
1987	£1 = $ ...

4   Find the current exchange rate and try to represent it on your graph.

5   **Investigate** the effect of the different exchange rates on **a** Americans visiting Britain.
    b Britons visiting America.

Visitors to Britain (1948)

___ 5.2 Drawing graphs

To draw the straight line to represent two quantities, first work out two co-ordinates from the information you are given. Then plot these co-ordinates and draw the line. Look carefully at the example.

■ *EXAMPLE 1*

Draw a graph to represent an exchange rate of £1 to DM 3. Use a scale of 2 cm to £1 on the horizontal axis, and a scale of 2 cm to DM 5 on the vertical axis. From your graph, find:

a How many marks (DM) can be exchanged for £3.

b How many pounds can be exchanged for (i) DM 12 (ii) DM 18 (iii) DM 180.

From the information given:

£1 is equivalent to DM 3

Therefore £5 is equivalent to DM 3 × 5 = DM 15

Table of data

£	0	5
DM	0	15

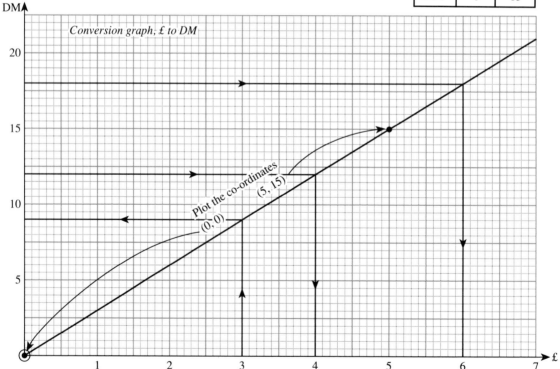

From the graph:

a £3 is equivalent to DM 9.

b (i) DM 12 is equivalent to £4 (ii) DM 18 is equivalent to £6
(iii) DM 180 is equivalent to £6 × 10 = £60.

REMEMBER

When drawing a graph:

1 If necessary, work out a table of data from the information given.

2 Draw the axes, divide each into equal parts using the given scale and label clearly.

3 Plot each point with a neat cross and join up with a straight line.

4 Give the graph a title.

5 Use a sharp pencil and do not press too hard.

Exercise 34

1 This table shows the cost of a certain kind of apple.

Weight (kg)	2	4	6
Cost (p)	80	160	240

Show this information on a graph using a horizontal scale of 2 cm to 1 kg and a vertical scale of 2 cm to 20p.

a Use the graph to find the cost of (i) 3 kg (ii) 5 kg (iii) $\frac{1}{2}$ kg and (iv) $2\frac{1}{2}$ kg of apples.

b Use the graph to find the weight of apples which could be bought for (i) 80p (ii) £1.80 (iii) 60p (iv) £1.40.

2 This table shows the cost of paraffin.

Paraffin (litres)	5	15	25
Cost (£)	1	3	5

Plot a graph of this information using a horizontal scale of 2 cm to 5 litres and a vertical scale of 2 cm to £1.

a Use the graph to find the cost of (i) 21 litres (ii) 17 litres (iii) 3 litres (iv) 22.5 litres.

b Use the graph to find the quantity of paraffin which could be bought for (i) £1.50 (ii) £3.50 (iii) £2.20 (iv) £1.40 (v) £4.80.

3 Before going on holiday to Spain, Winston produced this table of money equivalents.

Pounds	1	20	50	80
Pesetas	250	5000	12 500	20 000

Draw a graph to illustrate this information using a scale of 2 cm to £20 on the horizontal axis, and a scale of 2 cm to Ptas 5000 on the vertical axis. Find from your graph:

a How many pesetas can be exchanged for (i) £30 (ii) £90 (iii) £44 (iv) £28 (v) £32.

b How many pounds can be exchanged for (i) Ptas 17 500 (ii) Ptas 12 500 (iii) Ptas 2500 (iv) Ptas 16 000 (v) Ptas 12 000.

4 A teacher has marked an examination out of 120 and wishes to convert each mark to a percentage. Draw a graph for this purpose. Use a scale of 2 cm to 20 marks on both axes, using the horizontal axis for the marks out of 120. Find from your graph:

  a The percentage marks corresponding to (i) 72   (ii) 84   (iii) 36   (iv) 108   (v) 48   (vi) 102, marks out of 120.

  b The marks out of 120 which give (i) 75%   (ii) 25%   (iii) 80%   (iv) 45%   (v) 65% (vi) 35%.

5 Assume a telephone call to India costs £2.50 for 1 minute. Draw a graph to represent this information. Use a horizontal scale of 2 cm to 20 minutes and a vertical scale of 2 cm to £1.

  a Find the time of a call which costs (i) £3   (ii) £4   (iii) £1.50   (iv) £25.

  b Find the cost of a call which lasts (i) 24 seconds   (ii) 1 minute and 24 seconds
    (iii) 2 minutes and 12 seconds   (iv) 3 minutes and 36 seconds.

6 Given that 15 kilometres is the same distance as 8 nautical miles, draw a graph which converts kilometres to nautical miles. Use a horizontal scale of 2 cm to 200 km and a vertical scale of 2 cm to 100 nautical miles.

  a Use your graph to convert the following distances to nautical miles:

  (i) New Orleans to Havana, 1200 km   (ii) Hull to Stavanger, 900 km

  (iii) Liverpool to Belfast, 300 km   (iv) Bristol to Cork, 450 km.

  b Use your graph to convert the following distances to kilometres:

  (i) Newcastle to Bergen, 400 nautical miles   (ii) Hull to Esjberg, 320 nautical miles

  (iii) Weymouth to Guernsey, 80 nautical miles   (iv) Gibraltar to Marseille, 720 nautical miles.

7 It is estimated that throughout the World man destroys 300 km^2 of forest per day.

Using a scale of 2 cm to 5 days on the horizontal axis, and 2 cm to 1000 km^2 on the vertical axis, draw a graph to represent this relationship.

The areas of certain British counties are given below. Use your graph to find the time taken for man to destroy an equivalent area of forest for each case.

  a Lancashire   3000 km^2
  b Northamptonshire   2400 km^2
  c Dorset   2700 km^2
  d Shropshire   3600 km^2
  e Kent   3900 km^2
  f Northumberland   5100 km^2
  g Strathclyde   13 500 km^2
  h Cornwall   3750 km^2
  i Gwent   1350 km^2

MASTERMINDERS

8 Railway journeys cost 20p per mile and motorway coach journeys cost 8p per mile. Using a scale of 2 cm to 20 miles on the horizontal axis, and a scale of 2 cm to £5 on the vertical axis, draw two graph lines in order to illustrate the two rates.

   a Find from your graph how much further you could travel by motorway coach for £12.
   b Find the extra price of travelling by rail for a journey of (i) 150 miles (ii) 225 miles.
   c The mean speed of the train and coach is 100 mph (miles per hour or miles/hour) and 60 mph respectively. For how much longer could you travel on the coach if each fare was £12?

9 A Rolls Royce travels for 10 minutes on 5 litres of petrol when travelling at 90 km/h. A Lada travels for 10 minutes on only 1 litre of petrol, when travelling at the same speed. Using a scale of 2 cm to 10 minutes on the horizontal axis, and a scale of 2 cm to 2 litres on the vertical axis, draw two graph lines in order to illustrate the two rates of fuel consumption.
Find from your graph:
   a How much longer the Lada would travel on 7.5 litres of petrol.
   b How much longer and how much further the Lada would travel on 5 litres of petrol.
   c How much more petrol the Rolls Royce would consume during a journey which lasted 20 minutes.
   d How much more petrol the Rolls Royce would consume during a journey of length (i) 15 km (ii) 37.5 km.

10 In flight, Concorde uses 30 000 litres of fuel every hour. At full speed, the QE2 uses 25 000 litres of fuel every half-hour. Using a scale of 2 cm to 10 minutes on the horizontal axis, and a scale of 2 cm to 10 000 litres on the vertical axis, draw two graph lines in order to illustrate the two rates. Find:
   a How much longer Concorde travels on (i) 25 000 litres   (ii) 37 500 litres.
   b How much more fuel the QE2 consumes while travelling for (i) 30 minutes   (ii) 75 minutes.
   c How much fuel Concorde consumes in crossing the Atlantic if the flight lasts $3\frac{1}{2}$ hours.
   d How long the QE2 takes to cross the Atlantic, if it consumes 6 000 000 litres of fuel in doing so.

___ *Activity 14*

Find information relating two quantities together. Draw a suitable graph to illustrate this relationship.

___ 5.3 Using graphs

Sometimes a graph is not a single straight line. In this section we work from and draw such graphs.

___ Exercise 35

1   The table shows how much snow had fallen at hourly intervals on a certain day. The graph illustrates the information.

Time	Depth of snow	Time	Depth of snow	Time	Depth of snow
6:00 am	0 cm	10:00 am	14 cm	2:00 pm	26 cm
7:00 am	4 cm	11:00 am	16 cm	3:00 pm	30 cm
8:00 am	6 cm	12:00 pm	16 cm	4:00 pm	32 cm
9:00 am	8 cm	1:00 pm	18 cm		

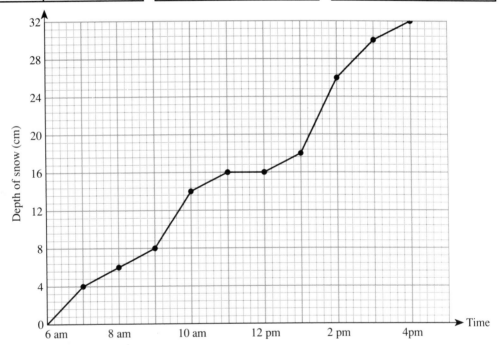

a Find the hourly interval in which no snow fell.

b Find the hourly interval which had the greatest snowfall and how much this was.

c What was the mean rate of snowfall between 6 am and 2 pm?

d What was the mean rate of snowfall between 12 pm and 4 pm?

e Find the number of cubic metres of snow which fell on a football pitch between 6 am and 4 pm if the dimensions of the pitch were 80 m by 40 m.

f Find the depth of the fallen snow at: (i) 6:30 am (ii) 2:30 pm (iii) 1:30 pm (iv) 8:30 am.

2 The central heating system in Marta's house is operated by a time switch, which turns it on and off twice each day.

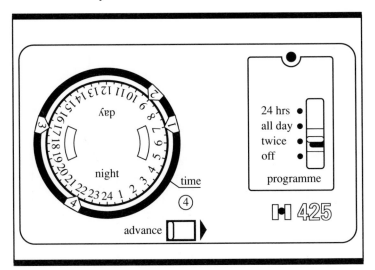

One day Marta stays at home and measures the temperatures at hourly intervals from 05:00 to 24:00, as shown in the table below.

Time	Temperature	Time	Temperature	Time	Temperature
05:00	2 °C	12:00	11 °C	19:00	22 °C
06:00	2 °C	13:00	9 °C	20:00	22 °C
07:00	14 °C	14:00	8 °C	21:00	22 °C
08:00	22 °C	15:00	7 °C	22:00	22 °C
09:00	18 °C	16:00	6 °C	23:00	19 °C
10:00	15 °C	17:00	17 °C	24:00	16 °C
11:00	13 °C	18:00	21 °C		

Using a horizontal scale of 1 cm to 1 hour, and a vertical scale of 1 cm to 2° C, plot these details on a graph.

From your graph, find:
a The times at which the heating is turned on.
b The times at which the heating is turned off.
c The hourly interval during which the temperature rose most quickly, and by how many degrees it rose.
d The hourly interval during which the temperature fell most quickly, and by how many degrees it fell.
e The mean rate at which the temperature falls per hour after the heating has been turned off.
f The temperature at each of the following times:
  (i) 06:30   (ii) 07:30
  (iii) 08:30   (iv) 10:30
  (v) 17:30   (vi) 09:30
  (vii) 13:30   (viii) 22:30

3 Coffee is sold at a fête which lasts from 2 pm to 6 pm. The graph shows the amount of coffee in the urn at half-hourly intervals.

The coffee is sold, in cups of capacity 200 ml, at 40p per cup until 4 pm, after which it is sold at 20p per cup to avoid wastage. Copy and complete the table below.

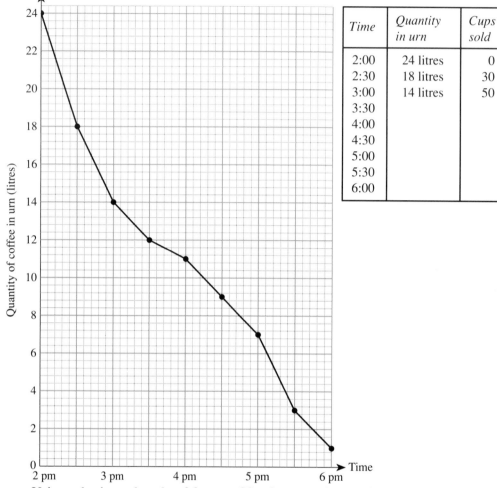

Time	Quantity in urn	Cups sold	Money collected
2:00	24 litres	0	0p
2:30	18 litres	30	£12
3:00	14 litres	50	£20
3:30			
4:00			
4:30			
5:00			
5:30			
6:00			

a Using a horizontal scale of 2 cm to 30 minutes and a vertical scale of 1 cm to 5 cups, plot a graph which shows the number of cups sold at each of the times shown in the table. Find from your graph the time by which (i) 15 cups (ii) 55 cups (iii) 80 cups (iv) 110 cups had been sold.

b Using a horizontal scale of 2 cm to 30 minutes and a scale of 1 cm to £1 in the vertical direction, plot a graph which shows the money collected at each of the times shown in the table. Find from your graph the money collected by (i) 5:15 pm (ii) 2:15 pm (iii) 2:45 pm.

4 Tom lives by the coast and he cycles 15 km to see his friend at Hill View Farm. On his way he has to cycle over Coastway Hill. The table on the page opposite shows details of his journey.

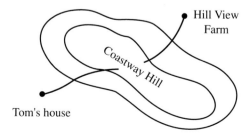

a Using a horizontal scale of 1 cm to 5 min, and a vertical scale of 1 cm to 10 m, draw a graph which shows altitude in terms of time. Find, from this graph:

(i) The number of metres through which he ascends per minute, when he is climbing Coastway Hill.

(ii) The number of metres through which he descends per minute, when he is riding down the far side of Coastway Hill.

Time from Tom's house	Distance from Tom's house	Altitude above sea level
0 min	0 km	0 m
20 min	6 km	0 m
45 min	10 km	100 m
50 min	12 km	20 m
60 min	15 km	20 m

b Using a horizontal scale of 1 cm to 5 min, and a vertical scale of 1 cm to 1 km, draw a graph which shows distance in terms of time. Find, from this graph:

(i) The speed at which he cycles on a level road.

(ii) The speed at which he cycles when he descends Coastway Hill.

(iii) The speed at which he cycles when he ascends Coastway Hill.

c Using a horizontal scale of 1 cm to 1 km, and a vertical scale of 1 cm to 10 m, draw a graph which shows altitude in terms of distance. Find from this graph:

(i) The ratio of the altitude of Coastway Hill to the distance he travels while ascending.

(ii) The ratio of the height through which Tom descends to the distance he travels while descending.

MASTERMINDER

5 Susan's father drives his car from Plymouth to London. Several details of his journey are shown in the table below.

Location	Time	Distance from Plymouth	Petrol in the tank
Plymouth	10:00	–	40 litres
Ashburton	11:00	40 km	35 litres
Exeter	11:30	80 km	31 litres
Wincanton	12:30	180 km	23 litres
Amesbury	13:30	240 km	18 litres
Fleet Services	14:30	300 km	12 litres
London	16:00	360 km	4 litres

a Using a horizontal scale of 2 cm to 1 hour, and a vertical scale of 1 cm to 2 litres, draw a graph which shows the quantity of petrol in the tank in terms of time.

b Using a horizontal scale of 2 cm to 50 km and a vertical scale of 1 cm to 2 litres, draw a graph which shows the quantity of petrol in the tank in terms of distance from Plymouth.

c Find from the first graph the mean rate at which petrol is consumed per hour.

d Find from the second graph, the mean number of kilometres travelled per litre of petrol consumed.

___ Revision Exercise 5A

1 A builders merchant sells strips of lead for £20 per metre.

a Copy and complete this table of data:

Length (m)	0	1	2	4
Cost (£)	0	20		

b Draw a graph to represent this information. Use a horizontal scale of 2 cm to £10 and a vertical scale of 2 cm to 1 m.

c Use your graph to find (i) the cost of 2.5 m, 1.75 m and 2.1 m, (ii) the length which is sold for £70, £25, £61.

2 The graph below shows the depth of water in a rainwater butt, in cm, between 01:00 and 04:30.

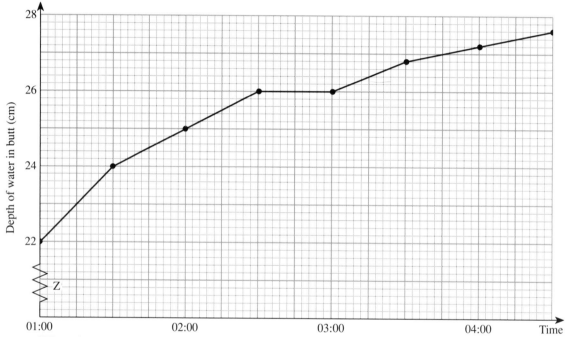

a What do you think the 'zigzag' line, marked Z, means?

b What was the depth of water in the butt at 02:00?

c What was the increase in depth between 01:30 and 03:00?

d Between which times was the depth increasing at the fastest rate?

e Between which times was there no increase in the depth?

f Explain how you would use the graph to show that at 01:15 the butt was filling at the rate of 4 cm/hour. Copy and complete the following table.

Time	Rate of increase in depth (cm/h)	Time	Rate of increase in depth (cm/h)
01:15 02:00	4	03:15 04:00	

Revision Exercise 5B

1   You are given that 5 miles is the same distance as 8 km. Draw a graph which converts kilometres to miles. Use a horizontal scale of 2 cm to 4 km, from 0 km to 28 km, and a vertical scale of 2 cm to 5 miles, from 0 miles to 20 miles.

   a Use your graph to convert (i) 20 km to miles   (ii) $2\frac{1}{2}$ miles to km   (iii) 18 km to miles
   (iv) 10.5 miles to km   (v) 1.5 miles to km   (vi) 280 km to miles.

   b A woman is driving at 50 km/h in a 30 miles/hour speed limit. Is she exceeding the speed limit and if so, by how much?

2   The graph below shows the height of an aircraft above the ground, in thousands of feet, between 10:00 and 15:00.

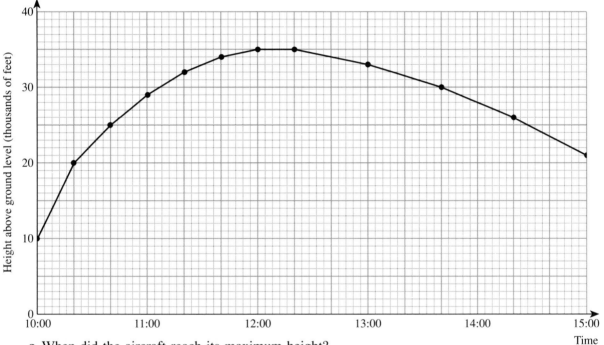

   a When did the aircraft reach its maximum height?
   b What was its height at 12:40?
   c For how long was the aircraft over 25 000 feet?
   d Write down the rate of ascent, in feet/minute, between 10:00 and 10:20.
   e What was the average rate of descent between 12:20 and 14:20?
   f What was the rate of descent at 12:40? If this rate were maintained, what time of day would the aircraft return to the ground?

___ Basics Test 5

A Calculator

1 $\dfrac{3.92}{3.82+3.18}$

2 Find $(3.82 + 3.18) \div 3.92$, to 2 SF.

3 Solve for a: $6.5a = 5.59$.

4 Simplify: $7.9y + 9.7y - 1.3y$.

5 Find the mean of: 0.5, 0.67, 0.76 and 0.53.

6 Change $\dfrac{969}{85}$ to a decimal.

B Paper and pencil

7 2.18×7

8 0.2×0.7

9 $20.4 - 17.06$

10 Solve for x: $\dfrac{15.6}{x} = 12$.

11 Simplify $6a \times 7$.

12 Simplify $7(6a + 7) - 50$.

13 Copy and complete: $\dfrac{}{5} = \dfrac{24}{60}$.

14 Solve for x: $\dfrac{x}{24} = \dfrac{5}{60}$.

15 Change $6500\,\text{cm}^2$ to m^2.

C Mental

Ten questions will be read out to you. Use the following facts to answer Questions 16 to 20.

16	**a** 1.5 m	**b** 1600 m	**c** 500 cm	**d** 9 m
17	**a** 0.3 km	**b** 2000 cm	**c** 20 m	**d** 5.3 m
18	**a** 8 mm	**b** 1.2 cm	**c** 2 mm	**d** 0.1 m
19	**a** A rabbit	**b** A shoe	**c** A bicycle	**d** A screwdriver
20	**a** A church spire	**b** A tall man	**c** A house	**d** A bungalow

___ Puzzlers

1 Find two numbers which when added together equal 41 but when subtracted equal 9.

2 Twenty teams enter a knock-out competition. How many matches are required to establish a winner?

3 In the diagram, ABCD is a square. By using **only** a ruler and pencil, make a copy of the diagram, but not necessarily the same size. Cut out the four pieces and fit them together to make the capital letter E.
(Hint: there are lots of parallel lines!)

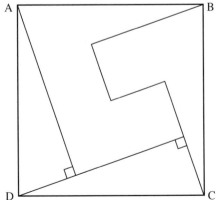

Coursework: Imperial to metric units

The graph on page 94 enables you to convert metric measures to Imperial (British) measures, or vice versa, in six different sets of units.

1 Use the graph to change:
   a 6 litres to gallons **b** 3.4 miles to km **c** 8.7 yards to m
   d 3.5 inches to cm **e** 5.4 square yards to m^2 **f** 5.3 kg to pounds.

2 Use the graph to change:
   a 1 litre to gallons **b** 1 km to miles **c** 1 m to yards
   d 1 cm to inches **e** 1 m^2 to square yards **f** 1 kg to pounds.

3 Use your answers to part 2 to write down the number of:
   a gallons in 5 litres **b** miles in 5 km **c** yards in 5 m
   d inches in 5 cm **e** square yards in 5 m^2 **f** pounds in 5 kg.

4 Use the graph to find the number of:
   a gallons in 5 litres **b** miles in 5 km **c** yards in 5 m
   d inches in 5 cm **e** square yards in 5 m^2 **f** pounds in 5 kg.

Explain why your answers to part 4 are likely to be more accurate than those in part 3. Compare your answers to the following, which have been worked out from more accurate information:

5 litres = 1.10 gallons   5 km = 3.11 miles   5 m = 5.47 yards
5 cm = 1.97 inches   5 m^2 = 5.98 square yards   5 kg = 11.0 pounds

5 A firm imports 5000 litres of brandy. It sells it on to a distributor at £40 per gallon.
   Investigate the effect, to the **importer**, of using your answer to part 3 **a** rather than to part 4 **a**.

EXTENSION

6 **a** Use the graph to answer the following:
   (i) Concorde uses 28 800 litres of fuel per hour. What is this in gallons per hour?
   (ii) The mean distance between the Earth and the Moon is 384 400 km. What is this in miles?
   (iii) The velocity of light is 186 325 miles/second. What is this velocity in km/second?
   b Make an accurate copy of the graph. Draw in the line which can be used to convert miles per gallon to kilometres per litre.

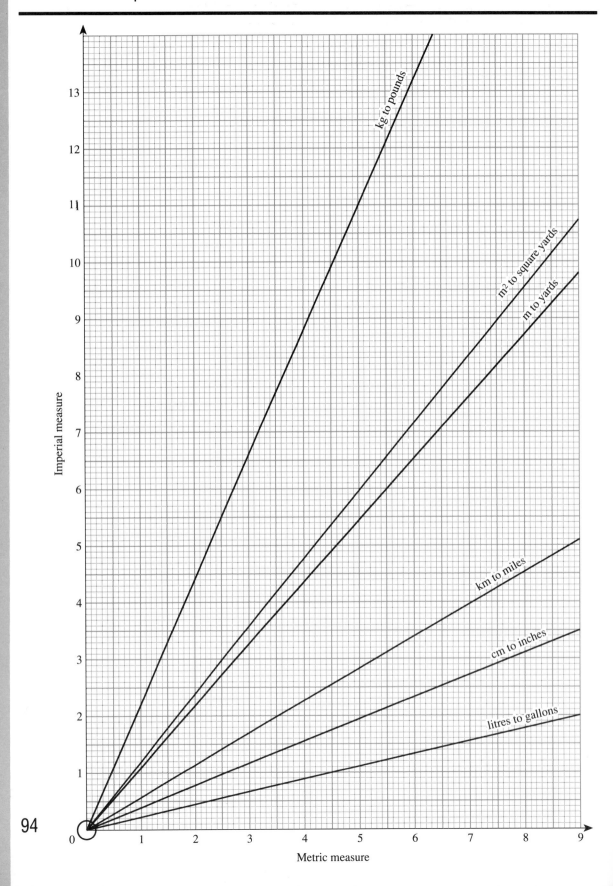

6 ALGEBRA II

6.1 Multiplication and division

Multiplication

We have seen in Chapter 2 that addition and subtraction are only possible with 'like terms' – so that $a + 2a = 3a$ but $a + 2b = a + 2b$.

Multiplication, however, is different. A **product** (the result of a multiplication), can always be expressed as a **single** term. Look at the rectangle.

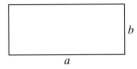

Perimeter $= a + b + a + b = 2a + 2b$

Area $= a \times b = ab$

(Note that the area **can** be expressed as a single term, whereas the perimeter **cannot**.)

Suppose the rectangle has sides of length $3a$ and $5b$, so its area is $3a \times 5b$.
$$3a \times 5b = 3 \times a \times 5 \times b$$
$$= 3 \times 5 \times a \times b$$
$$= 15ab$$

Look at these squares:

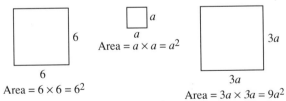

Area $= 6 \times 6 = 6^2$

Area $= a \times a = a^2$

Area $= 3a \times 3a = 9a^2$

Note also that:

$3 \times 3 \times 3 \times 3$ can be written as 3^4.
$7 \times 7 \times 7 \times 7 \times 7$ can be written as 7^5.
$a \times a \times a \times a$ can be written as a^4.

Therefore $(3a)^2 \times a^2 = 3a \times 3a \times a \times a$ means $9a^4$.

> **REMEMBER**
>
> $3b$ means '3 lots of b', which can be written $3 \times b$.
> Therefore $4 \times 3b$ means
> $4 \times 3 \times b = 12b$.

> **REMEMBER**
>
> $4 \times 3 \times 2$ can be written $2 \times 3 \times 4$ or $3 \times 2 \times 4$.
> Therefore $3b \times 5$ can be written $5 \times 3b = 15b$.

> **REMEMBER**
>
> • 6^2 means 6×6.
>   Therefore a^2 means $a \times a$.
> • $3a^2$ means $3 \times a \times a = 3 \times a^2$.
> • $(3a)^2$ means $3a \times 3a = 9a^2$.

After some practice, you may not find it necessary to write each term out as a product. Try to think about the principle and set each answer out as shown in Example 1.

■ *EXAMPLE 1*

Simplify: **a** $5x \times 3y \times 4z$ **b** $4p \times (3p)^2$

a $5x \times 3y \times 4z = 60xyz$

b $4p \times (3p)^2 \;= 4p \times 9p^2$
$\qquad\qquad\quad\; = 36p^3$

—— Exercise 36

Simplify Questions 1 to 10.

1 a $3 \times 2a$ **b** $4 \times 7x$ **c** $6 \times 8c$

2 a $3f \times 4$ **b** $3h \times 2$ **c** $7u \times 12$

3 a $2d \times e$ **b** $3a \times b$ **c** $5s \times t$

4 a $c \times c$ **b** $d \times d$ **c** $e \times e$

5 a $2x \times x$ **b** $3y \times y$ **c** $4r \times r$

6 a $3a \times 2a$ **b** $2b \times 4b$ **c** $5e \times 3e$

7 a $a^2 \times a$ **b** $d \times d^2$ **c** $g^2 \times g$

8 a $f^2 \times f$ **b** $h^2 \times h$ **c** $k^2 \times k^2$

9 a $2a^2 \times a$ **b** $3b \times b^2$ **c** $d^2 \times 3d$

10 a $3e^2 \times 2$ **b** $5t^2 \times 4$ **c** $5 \times 2e^2$

For Questions 11 to 13, find the area of the rectangle in terms of p.

11

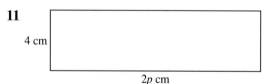

4 cm

$2p$ cm

12

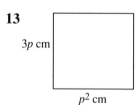

$3p$ cm

$2p$ cm

13

$3p$ cm

p^2 cm

Simplify Questions 14 to 23.

14 a $2t \times 3s$ **b** $4r \times 5t$ **c** $2t \times 3f$

15 a $b \times 3c$ **b** $g \times 5t$ **c** $h \times 5u$

16 a $4r \times s^2$ **b** $3d \times e^2$ **c** $5h \times j^2$

17 a $x^2 \times 2d$ **b** $b^2 \times 2a$ **c** $c^2 \times 3m$

18 a $2a^2 \times b^2$ **b** $3v^2 \times 3u^2$ **c** $2d^2 \times 2e$

19 a $2y \times 2y \times y$ **b** $4 \times 3r \times 2r$ **c** $3w \times 3x \times z$

20 a $q \times 2q \times 3q$ **b** $3a \times 3a \times 4a$ **c** $z^2 \times 2 \times z$

21 **a** $2d \times d^2 \times e$ **b** $a^2 \times b^2 \times c$ **c** $3a^2 \times a \times 2b$

22 **a** $2x^2 \times 3 \times 2x$ **b** $3e \times e^2 \times e$ **c** $4f \times 4f \times 4f$

23 **a** $(2a)^2 \times a$ **b** $(3b)^2 \times 3b$ **c** $(4m)^2 \times m^2$

24 Find the volume of the cuboid in terms of p.

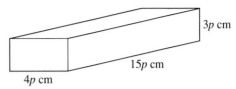

3p cm

15p cm

4p cm

25 Find the volume of a cuboid in terms of x and y, if it is $6y$ cm long, $5x$ cm high and $5x$ cm wide.

MASTERMINDERS

26 A cube has a side length of $2q$ cm. Find **a** its volume   **b** its total surface area   **c** the total length of its edges.

27 Simplify: **a** $2e \times (2e)^2 \times 2e^3 \times 2$ **b** $(2a^2)^2 \times (2a)^3$ **c** $(ab^2)^2 \times (ba^2)^2 \times a^2b^2$

▬ Division

Division is like multiplication. If one term is divided by another, the result can be always expressed as a **single** term.

> **REMEMBER**
>
> $a \div b$ means $\frac{a}{b}$.

The diagram shows a square floor. The area of the floor is a^2 square metres, and the total cost of carpeting is £x.

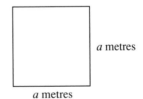

a metres

a metres

So the cost of carpeting each square metre

$$= \frac{\text{Total cost}}{\text{Area}} = £\frac{x}{a^2}$$

■*EXAMPLE 2*

Simplify **a** $x \div 5x$ **b** $45m \div 25m^2$ **c** $30p^2q^2 \div 48p$

a $x \div 5x = \dfrac{x}{5x}$ (Cancel by x)

            $= \dfrac{1}{5}$

b $45m \div 25m^2 = \dfrac{45m}{25m^2}$ (Cancel by $5m$)

                $= \dfrac{9}{5m}$

c $\quad 30p^2q^2 \div 48p \quad = \dfrac{30p^2q^2}{48p} \quad$ (Cancel by $6p$)

$$= \dfrac{5pq^2}{8}$$

___ Exercise 37

1 Simplify: **a** $\dfrac{3x}{x}$ **b** $\dfrac{3x}{3}$ **c** $\dfrac{6y}{6}$ **d** $\dfrac{7v}{v}$

2 Simplify: **a** $\dfrac{ab}{a}$ **b** $\dfrac{xy}{y}$ **c** $\dfrac{mn}{m}$ **d** $\dfrac{xy}{xy}$

3 Simplify: **a** $\dfrac{6x}{3}$ **b** $\dfrac{12y}{4}$ **c** $\dfrac{4ab}{2}$ **d** $\dfrac{6cd}{12}$

4 Simplify: **a** $\dfrac{2y^2}{2}$ **b** $\dfrac{x^2}{x}$ **c** $\dfrac{3a^2}{a^2}$ **d** $\dfrac{6b^2}{b}$

5 Simplify: **a** $\dfrac{4x^2}{4x}$ **b** $\dfrac{6a^2}{2a}$ **c** $\dfrac{12c^2}{4c^2}$ **d** $\dfrac{10d^2}{10d}$

6 Simplify: **a** $\dfrac{y}{2y}$ **b** $\dfrac{3}{3b}$ **c** $\dfrac{a}{a^2}$ **d** $\dfrac{b}{2b}$

7 Simplify: **a** $\dfrac{2a}{4a^2}$ **b** $\dfrac{7a}{21a^2}$ **c** $\dfrac{9}{27x^2}$ **d** $\dfrac{ab}{3b^2}$

8 The area of the rectangle is $24a^2$ square metres. Find its width in terms of a.

$8a$ metres

9 A rectangular floor measures $20x$ metres by $15x$ metres. Find the area of the floor in terms of x. What is the cost of carpet per square metre in terms of x if the total cost is £930?

10 Simplify: **a** $12a \div 8a$ **b** $27b^2 \div 30b$ **c** $\dfrac{28c^3}{35c}$ **d** $\dfrac{30d^3}{36d^3}$

11 Simplify: **a** $12m \div 20m^2$ **b** $40n \div 32n^3$ **c** $28p^2 \div 16p^3$ **d** $3x^2 \div 3x^3$

12 Simplify: **a** $25pq \div 40q$ **b** $18mn \div 30m$ **c** $27xy^2 \div 60x$ **d** $35uv^2 \div 40v$

13 Simplify: **a** $\dfrac{54ab^2}{24ab}$ **b** $\dfrac{45p^2q^2}{30p}$ **c** $16m^2n^2 \div 80n$ **d** $75c^2d^2 \div 300cd^2$

MASTERMINDERS

14 Simplify: **a** $\dfrac{150a^2b^2}{400a^2b}$ **b** $\dfrac{45y^2z^2}{150yz}$ **c** $\dfrac{52ab^2c^3}{65a^3b^2c}$ **d** $\dfrac{221(2a^5)^3b^{10}}{34(13b^3)^3a^{14}}$

15 The square base of a cuboid has an area of $9a^2$ cm^2. If its volume is $135a^3$ cm^3, find its total surface area.

16 **Investigate** $a \div b \div c$.

— 6.2 Fractions

Before starting this section, make sure that you are able to work out simple arithmetic fractions (look back to page 2 if necessary).

— Multiplication and division

■ *EXAMPLE 1*

Simplify **a** $\frac{a}{4} \times 3$ **b** $\frac{b}{3} \div \frac{6}{a}$ **c** $\frac{2a}{3} \div \frac{4a}{9}$

a $\frac{a}{4} \times \frac{3}{1} = \frac{3a}{4}$

b $\frac{b}{3} \div \frac{6}{a} = \frac{b}{3} \times \frac{a}{6} = \frac{ab}{18}$

c $\frac{2a}{3} \div \frac{4a}{9} = \frac{2a}{3} \times \frac{9}{4a} = \frac{3}{2} = 1\frac{1}{2}$

> REMEMBER
>
> To divide by a fraction: turn it upside down and multiply.

— Exercise 38

Simplify all the expressions in this exercise.

1 $\frac{a}{6} \times 5$
2 $4 \times \frac{x}{8}$
3 $\frac{y}{2} \times \frac{y}{3}$

4 $\frac{x}{2} \times \frac{a}{3}$
5 $\frac{3}{4} \times \frac{a}{3}$
6 $\frac{c}{9} \div \frac{c}{3}$

7 $\frac{1}{3} \div \frac{x}{6}$
8 $\frac{y}{5} \div \frac{1}{2}$
9 $\frac{b}{4} \div \frac{b}{4}$

10 $\frac{3x}{4} \div \frac{x}{8}$
11 $\frac{2a}{3} \times \frac{9}{4}$
12 $\frac{p}{5} \times \frac{15}{16}$

13 $x \times \frac{y}{4}$
14 $a \times \frac{a}{3}$
15 $4 \times \frac{ab}{8}$

16 $4 \div \frac{8}{ab}$
17 $\frac{2a}{5} \div \frac{3a}{10}$
18 $\frac{b}{8} \div 3$

19 $xy \div \frac{xy}{2}$
20 $\frac{4x}{5} \times \frac{4x}{5}$
21 $\frac{2x}{3} \div \frac{2x}{3}$

MASTERMINDERS

22 $\frac{x^2}{4} \times \frac{2y}{x} \times \frac{8}{y^3}$
23 $\frac{2xy}{9} \times \frac{27}{x^2} \div \frac{y}{3}$
24 $5\frac{1}{4}ab \times \frac{3}{7b}$

25 $3\frac{3}{5}xyz^2 \times \frac{5}{6zx}$
26 $\frac{8abc}{15de^2} \div \frac{24c}{25e}$
27 $3\frac{1}{4}x^2y \times \frac{3}{xy} \div 9\frac{3}{4}x$

— Addition and subtraction

Algebraic fractions are like arithmetic fractions: they can only be added and subtracted if they are 'like terms'.

For example: $\frac{a}{7} + \frac{a}{7} = \frac{2a}{7}$

and $\frac{2b}{9} - \frac{b}{9} = \frac{b}{9}$

If algebraic fractions do **not** have the same denominator, they must first be converted to 'like terms'.

For example: $\frac{x}{3} + \frac{x}{9} = \frac{3x}{9} + \frac{x}{9} = \frac{4x}{9}$

(In this example we have multiplied both numerator and denominator of $\frac{x}{3}$ by 3, that is:

$\frac{x \times 3}{3 \times 3} = \frac{x}{3} \times \frac{3}{3} = \frac{x}{3} \times 1$

In other words, we have not altered the **value** of the term $\frac{x}{3}$.)

> **REMEMBER**
>
> To add and subtract fractions: they must have the same denominators (they must be 'like terms').
>
> $\frac{2}{7} + \frac{1}{7} = \frac{3}{7}$ (arithmetic)
>
> $\frac{a}{8} + \frac{a}{8} = \frac{2a}{8} = \frac{a}{4}$ (algebraic)

— Exercise 39

Copy and complete:

1 $\frac{x}{2} = \frac{}{4}$ **2** $\frac{a}{2} = \frac{}{6}$ **3** $\frac{x}{3} = \frac{}{9}$

4 $\frac{b}{3} = \frac{}{12}$ **5** $\frac{m}{4} = \frac{}{8}$ **6** $\frac{c}{4} = \frac{}{16}$

7 $\frac{v}{5} = \frac{}{10}$ **8** $\frac{w}{1} = \frac{}{7}$ **9** $\frac{u}{7} = \frac{}{21}$

10 $\frac{3a}{4} = \frac{}{8}$ **11** $\frac{4b}{7} = \frac{}{14}$ **12** $\frac{6c}{13} = \frac{}{26}$

13 $\frac{ab}{5} = \frac{}{25}$ **14** $\frac{x^2}{1} = \frac{}{7}$ **15** $\frac{xy^2}{8} = \frac{}{24}$

MASTERMINDERS

16 $\frac{a}{b} = \frac{}{3b}$ **17** $\frac{x}{v} = \frac{}{vu}$ **18** $x^3 = \frac{}{4}$

19 $\frac{c^2}{b} = \frac{}{b^2}$ **20** $\frac{3b^2}{a} = \frac{}{a^2}$ **21** $\frac{4x^2}{y^2} = \frac{}{y}$

■ *EXAMPLE 2*

Simplify: **a** $\frac{x}{2} + \frac{3x}{4}$ **b** $\frac{a}{3} - \frac{b}{6}$ **c** $c + \frac{c}{3}$ **d** $\frac{v}{3} - \frac{u}{4}$

a $\frac{x}{2} + \frac{3x}{4} = \frac{2x}{4} + \frac{3x}{4} = \frac{5x}{4} = 1\frac{1}{4}x$

b $\frac{a}{3} - \frac{b}{6} = \frac{2a}{6} - \frac{b}{6} = \frac{2a-b}{6}$

c $c + \frac{c}{3} = \frac{c}{1} + \frac{c}{3} = \frac{3c}{3} + \frac{c}{3} = \frac{4c}{3} = 1\frac{1}{3}c$

d $\frac{v}{3} - \frac{u}{4} = \frac{4v}{12} - \frac{3u}{12} = \frac{4v-3u}{12}$

— Exercise 40

Simplify:

1 $\frac{a}{3} + \frac{a}{3}$

2 $\frac{b}{4} - \frac{b}{8}$

3 $\frac{c}{10} + \frac{c}{5}$

4 $\frac{d}{6} + \frac{5}{18}$

5 $x + \frac{x}{4}$

6 $y - \frac{y}{7}$

7 $\frac{3a}{8} - \frac{a}{4}$

8 $\frac{4b}{5} + \frac{3b}{10}$

9 $1 - \frac{a}{3}$

10 $\frac{a}{4} + \frac{a}{3}$

11 $\frac{c}{5} - \frac{c}{6}$

12 $\frac{3x}{5} + \frac{x}{4}$

13 $\frac{4y}{5} + \frac{5y}{4}$

14 $\frac{e}{6} + \frac{5e}{18}$

15 $2 - \frac{d}{3}$

16 $3 - \frac{2f}{3}$

17 $\frac{2f}{3} + 3$

18 $\frac{ab}{5} - \frac{ab}{7}$

MASTERMINDERS

19 $\frac{a}{2} + \frac{b}{3} + \frac{c}{4} + \frac{d}{5}$

20 $2 - \frac{3r}{4} + 3 - \frac{5r}{6}$

21 $\frac{t}{3} - \frac{t^2}{4} - \frac{t^3}{5} - \frac{t}{6}$

22 $\frac{x+a}{3} + \frac{a-2x}{6}$

23 $1 - \frac{x-y}{x}$

24 $2\frac{1}{3}x - \frac{x+y}{3}$

— 6.3 Factors

Most algebraic terms can be written as the product of 'factors'. For example:

The term $12a$ has factors $2, 2, 3, a$.

The term $8b$ has factors $2, 2, 2, b$.

Expressions which involve unlike terms can be simplified if they have a common factor. For example, look at this rectangle:

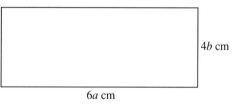

4b cm

6a cm

Perimeter $= 6a + 4b + 6a + 4b$

$\qquad = 12a + 8b$

$\qquad = 4(3a + 2b)\,\text{cm}$ (4 is the highest factor which occurs in both terms)

So in this case '4' is called the 'highest common factor' (HCF) of $12a$ and $8b$.

So we can say that the **factors** of $12a + 8b$ are 4 and $(3a + 2b)$.

┌— *REMEMBER*

The highest common factor (HCF) of two terms is the highest factor which occurs in both terms.

■ *EXAMPLE 1*

Factorize: **a** $21x - 15y$ **b** $15pq + 25pr$ **c** $3a^2b + 9ab^2 - 6abc$

a $21x - 15y = 3(7x - 5y)$ (The highest common factor is 3.)

b $15pq + 25pr = 5p(3q + 5r)$ (The highest common factor is $5p$.)

c $3a^2b + 9ab^2 - 6abc = 3ab(a + 3b - 2c)$ (The highest common factor is $3ab$.)

___ Exercise 41

Factorize Questions 1 to 14.

1 $9u + 12v$

2 $8y + 28z$

3 $35a - 45b$

4 $7c - 35d$

5 $3pq - 4pr$

6 $9xy + 16xz$

7 $8ab + 15a^2$

8 $12uv + 25v^2$

9 $15cd + 18c^2$

10 $24yz - 30y^2$

11 $40mn - 64n^2$

12 $15p^2 + 60pq$

13 $60r^2s + 24r^3$

14 $32x^3 - 80x^2y$

15 The area of the rectangle is $24pq\,\text{cm}^2$ and its length is $8q\,\text{cm}$.

8q cm

a Find the width in terms of p.

b Write down the perimeter in terms of p and q and factorize your answer.

16 Factorize $18x + 6v^2$, and hence simplify:

$$\frac{18x + 6v^2}{6}$$

MASTERMINDERS

Factorize Questions 17 to 24.

17 $35xy - 56yz + 105xz$

18 $48a^2bc + 72ab^2c + 112abc^2$

19 $24p^2q^2r + 120p^2qr^2 - 144pq^2r^2$

20 $v + v^2 + v^3 + v^4$

21 $\frac{x}{c} - x$

22 $\frac{a^2}{b} - a^3$

23 $\frac{ab}{x} - \frac{cd}{x}$

24 $x\sqrt{y} - 3\sqrt{y}$

25 A cuboid has a square base of side length $6a\,\text{cm}$. If its volume is $(144a^2b + 216a^2c + 180a^3)\,\text{cm}^3$, what is its height?

— **6.4** Substitution

When substituting directed numbers into expressions, great care must be taken with the signs. (If necessary, turn back to pages 14–17 for revision of directed numbers.)

■ *EXAMPLE 1*

If $a = -3$ and $b = -12$, work out: **a** $a^2 + b$ **b** $ab + a$ **c** $8a^2 \div b$ **d** $b^2 - a$

It is often helpful to put brackets around each term, for example, (-3) and (-12), when substituting:

a $a^2 + b = (-3)^2 + (-12) = 9 - 12 = -3$

b $ab + a = (-3) \times (-12) + (-3) = 36 - 3 = 33$

c $8a^2 \div b = \frac{8a^2}{b} = \frac{8 \times (-3) \times (-3)}{(-12)} = \frac{8 \times 9}{-12} = -6$

d $b^2 - a = (-12)^2 - (-3) = 144 + 3 = 147$

> *REMEMBER*
>
> When multiplying directed numbers:
> - **Like** signs give a **positive** result: $(-3) \times (-2) = +6$
> - **Unlike** signs give a **negative** result: $(-3) \times (+2) = -6$

— **Exercise 42**

1 If $a = 5$ and $b = -2$, find the value of:

a $a + b$	**b** $b + b$	**c** $b - a$	**d** ab
e $a \div b$	**f** $b \div a$	**g** a^2	**h** b^2

2 If $p = -3$ and $q = 4$, find the value of:

a $p + q$	**b** $p - q$	**c** pq	**d** $p \div q$
e p^2	**f** qp^2	**g** $p^2 \div q$	**h** pq^2

3 If $m = -10$ and $n = -8$, find the value of:

a $m + n$	**b** mn	**c** $\frac{m}{n}$	**d** $\frac{n}{m}$
e m^2	**f** nm^2	**g** $m^2 \div n$	**h** n^2

4 If $x = -30$, work out:

a $4x$	**b** $7x$	**c** $-3x$	**d** $-8x$
e $\frac{x}{6}$	**f** $\frac{x}{2}$	**g** $\frac{x}{-5}$	**h** $\frac{x}{-3}$

5   If $p = -3$ and $q = 5$, find the value of:

    a $3p + q$ **b** $8p + q$ **c** $4p - q$ **d** $9p - q$

    e $p^2 + q$ **f** $p + q^2$ **g** $p^2 - q$ **h** $p - q^2$

6   If $m = -2$ and $n = -7$, find the value of:

    a $3m + n$ **b** $n + 4m$ **c** $m^2 + n$ **d** $m + n^2$

    e $n^2 + m^2$ **f** $n^2 - m^2$ **g** $m^2 - n^2$ **h** $m^2 + m$

MASTERMINDERS

7   When $a = -1$ and $b = -2$, find the value of:

    a $b - 2a^2$ **b** $b - (2a)^2$ **c** $(b - 2a)^2$

8   When $a = -3$ and $b = -4$, find the value of:

    a $\dfrac{a^2 - b^2}{a - b}$

    b $\dfrac{(a - b)^2}{a - b}$

    c $\dfrac{b^2 - a^2}{(b - a)^2}$

    d $\dfrac{b^2 - a^2}{(b - a)(b + a)}$

___ 6.5 Equations

Equations help us to solve a variety of problems. Look carefully at the following examples.

■ EXAMPLE 1

The perimeter of a square is four times the length of one side.

a   If the side length is x cm, write down the perimeter in terms of x.

b   If the perimeter is 82 cm, write down an equation in x, and solve it to find x. Hence find the length of one side.

a   Perimeter $= 4x$

b $82 = 4x$ (Divide both sides by 4)

            $\frac{82}{4} = x$

            $x = 20.5$

Therefore the side length of the square is 20.5 cm.

■ EXAMPLE 2

A farmer has y pigs. He has six more ducks than pigs.

a Write down, in terms of y, the number of ducks he has.

b Each pig has four legs and each duck has two legs. Write down, in terms of y, the total number of legs that his pigs and ducks have.

c If the total number of legs is 180, write down an equation in y and solve it to find (i) y (ii) the number of ducks he has.

a Number of ducks $= y + 6$

b Total number of legs $= 4y + 2(y + 6)$
$$= 6y + 12$$

c (i) $\qquad 180 = 6y + 12 \quad$ (Subtract 12 from both sides and then divide both sides by 6)

$$\frac{180 - 12}{6} = y$$

$$y = 28$$

(ii) Therefore the number of ducks $= y + 6 = 28 + 6 = 34$

▬ Exercise 43

1 Fred bought a bicycle for £95 and sold it to give him a profit of £b.
a Write down, in terms of b, the selling price.
b If the selling price was £137, write down an equation in b, and solve it to find the value of b and hence the profit.

2 Mr Smith bought an old lawn mower for £128 and sold it for a profit for £c.
a Write down, in terms of c, the profit he made.
b If he made a profit of £26 write down an equation in c, and solve it to find the value of c and hence the selling price.

3 Siobhan is d years old and her father is three times older than Siobhan.
a Write down, in terms of d, her father's age.
b If her father is 43.5 years old, write down an equation in d, and solve it to find the value of d and hence Siobhan's age.

4 Tariq's mother is f years old and is three times older than Tariq.
a Write down, in terms of f, Tariq's age.
b If Tariq is 11 years old, write down an equation in f, and solve it to find the value of f and hence Tariq's mother's age.

5 A car travels at 30 mph for x hours.
a Write down, in terms of x, the distance travelled.
b If the distance travelled was 22.5 miles, find the value of x and hence the time taken.

6 Janil cycles at 12 mph for a distance of y miles.

a Write down, in terms of y, the time taken.

b If the total time taken was $1\frac{1}{4}$ hours, find the value of y and hence the distance cycled.

7 In class 3A there are $2x$ girls and $(x+9)$ boys.

In class 3B there are $3x$ boys and $(x+11)$ girls.

If there is a total of 48 in both classes, find the value of x and hence the total number of boys in 3A and 3B.

8 A bus company has $3y$ small buses and $(y+30)$ large buses. If the total number of buses is $10y$, find the value of y and hence the number of large buses.

9 Katie is t years old now. Her brother Elliott is four times as old as Katie.

a Find, in terms of t, how old:

   (i) Elliott is now.

   (ii) Elliott will be in five years time.

   (iii) Katie will be in five years time.

b If, in five years time, Elliott will be twice as old as Katie, write down an equation for t and solve it to find the value of t and hence Elliott's present age.

10 At a snack bar a cheese sandwich costs x pence. A ham sandwich costs 30p more.

a Write down, in terms of x, the cost of a ham sandwich.

b If three ham and four cheese sandwiches cost a total of £7.20, write down an equation for x and solve it to find the value of x and hence the cost of two cheese sandwiches.

MASTERMINDERS

11 Find three consecutive even numbers such that the sum of five times the largest and four times the middle number equals ten times the smallest.

12 Two years ago my age was four times that of my son. Eight years ago my age was ten times that of my son. Find my son's age.

13 The length of a room is $1\frac{1}{2}$ times its width. A carpet, which is twice as long as it is wide, is placed in the centre of the room and leaves a border 1 metre wide all around. Find the area of the carpet.

Revision Exercise 6A

1 Simplify **a** $4a \times 2$ **b** $3b \times 2b$.
2 Find, in terms of x:
  a The perimeter of the rectangle.
  b The area of the rectangle.

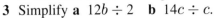

x cm

$3x$ cm

3 Simplify **a** $12b \div 2$ **b** $14c \div c$.
4 Simplify **a** $\frac{d}{4} \times 2$ **b** $3 \div \frac{x}{6}$.
5 Copy and complete **a** $\frac{x}{4} = \frac{}{8}$ **b** $\frac{ab}{7} = \frac{}{21}$.
6 Simplify **a** $\frac{x}{5} + \frac{x}{5}$ **b** $\frac{v}{4} - \frac{v}{8}$.
7 Factorize **a** $2x - 6$ **b** $6ab - 2b$.
8 When $a = -2$ and $b = -3$, find the value of **a** $2ab$ **b** $a - b$.
9 The rectangle represents a carpet of area $12x\,\text{m}^2$ and width $2x\,\text{m}$.
  a Find the length of the carpet.
  b If the actual area of the carpet is $24\,\text{m}^2$, find its width.

$2x$ m

10 Maggie is x years old. Douglas is two years older than Maggie.
  a Write down, in terms of x, (i) Douglas's age (ii) their combined age.
  b If their combined age is 72 years, write down an equation involving x and solve it to find the value of x. Use your answer to find Douglas's age.

Revision Exercise 6B

1 Simplify **a** $2y \times y$ **b** $2y \div y$.
2 Find, in terms of x:
  a The perimeter of the rectangle.
  b The area of the rectangle.

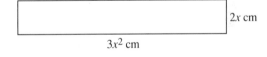

$2x$ cm

$3x^2$ cm

3 Simplify **a** $3a^2 \times 2a^2$ **b** $(3a)^2 \div 3a$.
4 Simplify **a** $\frac{x^2}{2} \times \frac{4}{x}$ **b** $\frac{2b^2}{a} \div \frac{ab}{3}$.
5 When $a = -2$ and $b = -3$, find the value of **a** $\frac{a+b}{a-b}$ **b** $ab - a^2$.
6 Simplify **a** $\frac{a}{3} + \frac{b}{2}$ **b** $\frac{2x}{5} - \frac{3x}{2}$.
7 Factorize **a** $15ax - 30a^2$ **b** $6ab^2 + 3ba^2$.
8 In a coach party there are four more adults than children.
  a If there are x children, how many people are there altogether?
  b The charge is £8 for each adult and £5 for each child. Write down an expression for the total cost in terms of x.
  c If the total cost is £422, find the number of children in the party.
9 ABCD represents a picture surrounded by a frame of width x cm.
  a Write down, in terms of x, the length of (i) AB (ii) BC.
  b Write down, in terms of x, the area of (i) the picture
    (ii) the frame and the picture (iii) the frame.
  c If the frame has an area of $160\,\text{cm}^2$, find its width.

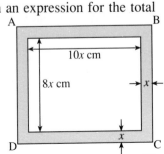

A   B
$10x$ cm
$8x$ cm
x
x
D   C

__ Basics Test 6

A Calculator

    1 Which is the largest: $\frac{5}{7}$, 0.714 28, 72%?   **2** Solve for x: $3.2 = \frac{x}{9}$.

    3 Solve for y, to 2 SF: $9 = 4 \div y$.   **4** $\frac{3.8}{2.9+1.4}$ to 2 SF.

    5 Change $\frac{1}{19}$ to a decimal, correct to 2 DP.   **6** $\frac{9}{24} + 0.035$.

B Paper and pencil

    7 Simplify $4a \times a$.   **8** Simplify $4a \div a$.

Use the fact that $79 \times 24 = 1896$ to work out questions 9, 10 and 11.

    9 7.9×2.4 **10** 0.79×240 **11** $1896 \div 2.4$

    12 What is 46% of £28?   **13** What is 3 out of 40 as a percentage?

    14 Change $467\,000\,\text{cm}^3$ to m^3.   **15** Change 27 minutes to a decimal of one hour.

C Mental

Ten questions will be read out to you. You will need the following information to answer Questions 16 to 21.

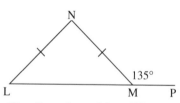

(For Questions 16 to 17)

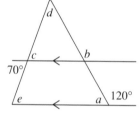

(For Questions 18 to 21)

__ Puzzlers

1 How many numbers from 1 to 100 have a digit 6 in them?

2 Show by any simple means that $1\,000\,000\,123\,456$ is not a perfect square.

3 Use your calculator to help work out the exact value of

$$\frac{999\,999\,999 \times 999\,999\,999}{1+2+3+4+5+6+7+8+9+8+7+6+5+4+3+2+1}$$

Coursework: A paper-folding problem

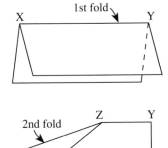

In this Coursework, we are going to investigate five different shapes which can be cut out from a rectangular piece of paper. Remember to draw diagrams to illustrate your answers.

Fold the paper three times as shown in Figure 1.

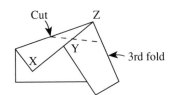

Figure 1

1   Use this process to try to cut out each of the shapes below. Label each as shown.

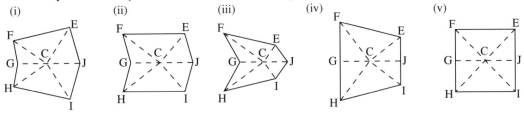

2   By looking at the properties of your five cut-outs, explain why:
    a Angle ECF is always 90°.
    b JI is always parallel to GH.

3   Make a large copy of shape (i). On it mark the angle FGC with the letter '*a*' and the angle JCE with the letter '*b*'. Write down, in terms of *a* and *b*, the angles:
    a CĜH   **b** JĈI   **c** EĴC   **d** FĈG   **e** JÊC   **f** CÊF   **g** GF̂C   **h** CF̂E

4   When answering this part of the Coursework, look carefully at your five cut-outs. Copy the following statements and indicate which are 'always true', which are 'sometimes true' and which are 'never true'.
    a EC = CI   **b** EF = IH   **c** CĜF = CĜH
    d CĴE = 90°   **e** △ECF is isosceles **f** JC is not equal to CG
    g EF is parallel to IH   **h** EJ + FG = EF   **i** EĈH = 180°
    j EĴI = FĈH   **k** EFGHIJ is a rectangle   **l** JĈI = 45°
    m JE = EF

EXTENSION

5   **Investigate** the properties of the five shapes when the cut is
    a At right angles to XYZ.
    b Not at right angles to XYZ (see Figure 1).

7 ARITHMETIC II

7.1 Index form

We already know that $10 \times 10 \times 10 \times 10 = 10^4$. In words, we say this is '10 to the power 4'. 10^4 can be described as a term which is expressed in 'index form'. (The plural of index is indices.)

We use indices in order to make it simpler to write and use very large and very small numbers.

Very large numbers

Look carefully at the number below, which shows the approximate distance in miles from the Earth to the remotest known star. What is beyond this star may never be discovered.

Earth   Quasar OQ172

10 000 000 000 000 000 000 000 miles

Can you see why this very large number can be written as 10^{22}?

The following names are used for very large numbers:

> **NOTE**
>
> | | SI prefixes |
> |---|---|
> | 1 billion $= 1\,000\,000\,000 = 10^9$ | giga G |
> | 1 trillion $= 1\,000\,000\,000\,000 = 10^{12}$ | tera T |
> | 1 quadrillion $= 1\,000\,000\,000\,000\,000 = 10^{15}$ | peta P |

(SI stands for the International System of Units, widely used in science, and recognised throughout the world.)

Exercise 44

1 Copy and complete the table.

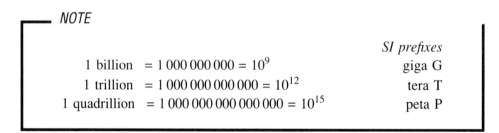

Number	Product form in terms of 10	Index form
1 million		
100 000		
10 000	$10 \times 10 \times 10 \times 10$	10^4
	$10 \times 10 \times 10$	
	10×10	
	10	
1	Not possible	10^0

For Questions 2 to 10, copy the pairs of numbers and insert the correct sign, $>$, $<$ or $=$, between each pair. ($>$ means 'greater than'. $<$ means 'less than'.)

2 10^4 and 10^5

3 10^4 and 1 thousand

4 10^4 and 10 thousand

5 10^5 and 1 million

6 10^5 and 100 thousand

7 5000 and 10^3

8 5000 and 10^4

9 600 000 and 10^6

10 40 000 and 10^4

For Questions 11 to 16, copy and complete the statement with the letters replaced by consecutive whole numbers.

11 60 lies between 10^p and 10^q.

12 5 million lies between 10^r and 10^s.

13 Half a million lies between 10^y and 10^z.

14 500 million lies between 10^t and 10^u.

15 30 million lies between 10^k and 10^l.

16 2000 million lies between 10^q and 10^r.

MASTERMINDER

17 It is said that the number of molecules in a cricket ball is the same as the number of cricket balls that would fit inside the Earth. If the volume of the Earth is a trillion times a trillion cubic metres, and that of a cricket ball is $100 \, \text{cm}^3$, find the number of molecules in a cricket ball.

__ *Activity 15*

The table below shows the very approximate area, in square miles, of eight regions on Earth. Copy and complete this table.

Region	Very approx. area in square miles	
	Number form	Index form
All the land on Earth	100 million	
North America	10 million	
Argentina	1 million	
British Isles	100 000	
Wales	10 000	
Gloucestershire	1000	
Isle of Wight	100	
Isles of Scilly	10	

1 How many times greater in area is all the land area on Earth than: **a** North America **b** the British Isles **c** Gloucestershire?

2 How many times would the area of Wales fit into: **a** the British Isles **b** Argentina **c** North America?

3 How many times would the area of the Isle of Wight fit into: **a** Wales **b** Argentina **c** North America?

4 The surface area of the largest star is about 10^{15} square miles. Write this area in **a** billions **b** trillions **c** quadrillions.

Activity 16

The table below shows the approximate distance, in miles, of four heavenly objects from the Earth. Copy and complete this table.

Celestial body	Approx. distance from Earth in miles	Number of times further from Earth than the Sun
Sun	10^8	1
Saturn	10^9	
Remotest visible star (Andromeda)	10^{19}	
Remotest known star (Quasar OQ172)	10^{22}	

1 Copy and complete:

   a ... is ten times further away than the Sun.

   b Andromeda is ... times further away than Saturn.

   c Quasar OQ172 is ... times further away than Andromeda.

   d Quasar OQ172 is ... times further away than the Sun.

2 To make a model showing the four distances from the Earth, a girl marks the Sun 1 cm from the Earth as shown:

Earth   Sun

Distance from Earth in miles

   a How far along the line should she place the other three celestial bodies?

   b If she had placed the Sun 1 mm from the Earth, how far along the line should she have placed the other three celestial bodies?

Very small numbers

Index form can also be used to represent numbers between 0 and 1, for example:

NOTE

$0.01 = \frac{1}{100}$ or $\frac{1}{10^2}$ *Index form:* 10^{-2}

$0.001 = \frac{1}{1000}$ or $\frac{1}{10^3}$ *Index form:* 10^{-3}

It is particularly useful for very small numbers. For example, the mass of an electron written out in full is:

   $0.000\,000\,000\,000\,000\,000\,000\,000\,000\,001\,\text{kg}$

Written in index form, this is $10^{-30}\,\text{kg}$.

Exercise 45

1 Copy and complete the table:

Decimal form	Fraction form	Index form
1	$\frac{1}{1}$	10^0
0.1		
0.01	$\frac{1}{100}$ or $\frac{1}{10^2}$	10^{-2}
0.001		
0.0001	$\frac{1}{10\,000}$ or $\frac{1}{10^4}$	10^{-4}
		10^{-5}
		10^{-6}

Copy the pairs of numbers and insert the correct sign, $>$, $<$ or $=$, between each pair.

2 0.001 and $\frac{1}{10\,000}$ 3 0.00001 and $\frac{1}{100\,000}$ 4 0.01 and 10^{-3} 5 0.00001 and 10^{-4}

6 0.0000001 and 10^{-6} 7 $\frac{1}{1000}$ and 10^{-3} 8 $\frac{1}{100}$ and 10^{-1} 9 $\frac{1}{10}$ and 10^{-2}

10 Copy the statements below with the letters replaced by consecutive whole numbers.
   a 0.0327 lies between 10^a and 10^b.   b 0.0003 lies between 10^c and 10^d.

Activity 17

The table shows the approximate mass, in kilograms, of four small objects. (The photograph shows a pigmy shrew, the world's smallest mammal.)

Object	Mass (kg)
House mouse	10^{-2}
Pigmy shrew	10^{-3}
Grain of sand	10^{-7}
Staphylococcus	10^{-15}

1 Write down the mass of each of the first three objects above, in grams, a in ordinary numbers   b in index form.

2 Copy and complete the following statements:
   a A house mouse is ... times heavier than a pigmy shrew.
   b A pigmy shrew is ... times heavier than a grain of sand.
   c A grain of sand is 100 000 times lighter than a ...
   d A pigmy shrew is 10 000 times heavier than a ...
   e A ... is 100 million times heavier than a ...
   f A house mouse is ... trillion times heavier than a ...

3 Copy each of the statements and insert the correct sign, $>$, $<$ or $=$.
   a The mass of 10 000 grains of sand is ☐ the mass of a house mouse.
   b The mass of 100 pigmy shrews is ☐ the mass of a house mouse.
   c The mass of 1000 grains of sand is ☐ the mass of a pigmy shrew.

__ 7.2 Standard form

You will now learn how to use index form to write any number. This is done by writing such numbers in 'standard form'.

NOTE

In standard form a number is written in the form

$$a \times 10^b$$

where a is 1 or greater than 1 but less than 10, and b is an integer.
(An integer is a whole number which can be negative and includes 0.)

■ *EXAMPLE 1*

Write in standard form **a** 48 000 **b** 0.000 48.

a 48 000 = 4.800 0 × 10 000
   = 4.8 × 10⁴

b 0.000 48 = 4.8 ÷ 10 000
   = 4.8 ÷ 10⁴
   = 4.8 × 10⁻⁴

■ *EXAMPLE 2*

Write as an ordinary number **a** 2.76×10^3 **b** 2.76×10^{-3}.

a $2.76 \times 10^3 = 2.76 \times 1000$
   $= 2760$

b $2.76 \times 10^{-3} = 2.76 \div 10^3$
   $= 2.76 \div 1000 = 0.002\,76$

It is easy to see why very large or very small numbers are often written in standard form when you look at the two examples below.

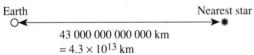

Earth   Nearest star

43 000 000 000 000 km
= 4.3×10^{13} km

The mass of an oxygen molecule is:
0.000 000 000 000 000 000 000 000 053 kg
= 5.3×10^{-26} kg

__ Exercise 46

For Questions 1 to 20, write in standard form:

1 3256	**2** 4410	**3** 5000	**4** 48 732	**5** 62 500
6 0.072	**7** 0.0364	**8** 0.0042	**9** 80 000	**10** 0.0085
11 0.007	**12** 0.0002	**13** 450	**14** 715	**15** 4000
16 7.9	**17** 100	**18** 0.01	**19** 1	**20** 1 million

For Questions 21 to 38, write as an ordinary number:

21 3.35×10^2 **22** 4.208×10^3 **23** 2.3456×10^4 **24** 8.7×10^1 **25** 1.36×10^3

26 7.5×10^3 **27** 6.4×10^{-1} **28** 3×10^{-1} **29** 5.156×10^4 **30** 2.7×10^4

31 5.6×10^0 **32** 3.725×10^{-2} **33** 5×10^{-5} **34** 3.6875×10^3 **35** 8.224×10^1

36 7.68×10^{-4} **37** 1×10^6 **38** 5.678×10^0

MASTERMINDER

39 The table below shows the length of each of a number of items in mm. Rearrange, copy and complete the table, with the lengths of the items arranged in descending order of size.

Item	Length (mm)	
	Standard form	Ordinary number
Bacterium		0.003 05
Wavelength of yellow light	5.896×10^{-4}	
Wavelength of a gamma ray	2.45×10^{-10}	
Electron diameter	5.6×10^{-12}	
Small insect		0.305
Wavelength of red light	6.562×10^{-4}	
Virus	9.144×10^{-6}	
Wavelength of violet light		0.000 43
Diameter of hydrogen atom	1.26×10^{-7}	
Wavelength of an X ray	1.54×10^{-7}	

■ EXAMPLE 3

Write each of the following in standard form correct to 2 SF: **a** 4090   **b** 0.0872.

a $4090 = 4.090 \times 1000$
$= 4.09 \times 10^3$
$= 4.1 \times 10^3$ to 2 SF.

b $0.0872 = 8.72 \div 100$
$= 8.72 \div 10^2$
$= 8.72 \times 10^{-2}$
$= 8.7 \times 10^{-2}$ to 2 SF.

___ Exercise 47

Write in standard form correct to 2 SF:

1 4197	**2** 6243	**3** 7560	**4** 17 180	**5** 52 750
6 327	**7** 974	**8** 436.8	**9** 620.4	**10** 385.1
11 700	**12** 2073	**13** 8036	**14** 5964	**15** 0.003 54
16 0.005 07	**17** 0.0415	**18** 0.0603	**19** 0.386	**20** 0.495

__ 7.3 Percentages

■ *EXAMPLE 1*

What percentages of the whole box of crisps are Plain,
Salt 'n' Vinegar and Roast Chicken?

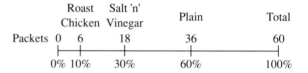

Total contents	60
Plain	36
Salt 'n' Vinegar	18
Roast Chicken	6

Percentage of Plain crisps $\quad = \frac{36}{60} \times 100 \quad = 60\%$

Percentage of Salt 'n' Vinegar $\quad = \frac{18}{60} \times 100 \quad = 30\%$

Percentage of Roast Chicken $\quad = \frac{6}{60} \times 100 \quad = 10\%$

You will see from this example that

$$60\% + 30\% + 10\% = 100\%$$

and that $\frac{36}{60} + \frac{18}{60} + \frac{6}{60} = 1$.

This example can be illustrated on a 'ratio line':

(Note: $\frac{6}{10} = \frac{18}{30} = \frac{36}{60} = \frac{60}{100}$, that is, the ratios are equal.)

This important fact enables us to use a ratio line to answer a variety of percentage questions. Look carefully at the following examples.

■ *EXAMPLE 2*

Mr Slim's weight before going on holiday was 40 kg. After his holiday his weight had increased by 12%. Find his new weight.

We are comparing his new weight with his original weight of 40 kg. Therefore we say his original weight is 100%. Let x = his new weight.

From this ratio line we can write:

$$\frac{40}{100} = \frac{x}{112}$$

$$112 \times 40 = 100x$$

$$\frac{112 \times 40}{100} = x$$

$$x = 44.8$$

Therefore his new weight is 44.8 kg.

116

■ *EXAMPLE 3*

In April Anna ran the 100 m in 13.40 seconds. In June she decreased her time by 5%. Find her improved time.

(We are comparing her new time with her original time of 13.40 seconds. Therefore we say her original time is 100%.) Let her improved time = x seconds.

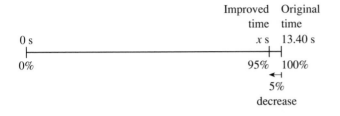

From this ratio line we can write:

$$\frac{x}{95} = \frac{13.40}{100}$$
$$100x = 13.40 \times 95$$
$$x = \frac{13.40 \times 95}{100}$$
$$x = 12.73$$

Therefore her improved time was 12.73 seconds.

■ *EXAMPLE 4*

A standard bottle of cough mixture contains 200 ml. The small bottle contains 50 ml less and the large bottle contains 70 ml more. Find, as a percentage, **a** how much less there is in the small bottle **b** how much more there is in the large bottle.

a   (We are comparing the capacity of the small bottle with the standard bottle. Therefore we say the standard size is 100%.)
The capacity of the small bottle is $(200 - 50)$ ml = 150 ml. Let x = 150 ml as a percentage.

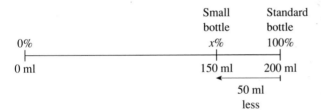

From this ratio line we can write:

$$\frac{x}{150} = \frac{100}{200}$$
$$200x = 100 \times 150$$
$$x = \frac{100 \times 150}{200}$$
$$x = 75$$

Therefore the small bottle contains 25% less than the standard bottle.

b   (We are comparing the capacity of the large bottle with the standard bottle. Therefore we say the standard bottle is 100%.)
The capacity of the large bottle is $(200 + 70)$ ml = 270 ml. Let y = 270 ml as a percentage.

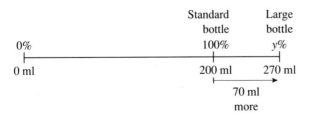

From this ratio line we can write:

$$\frac{100}{200} = \frac{y}{270}$$
$$270 \times 100 = 200y$$
$$\frac{270 \times 100}{200} = y$$
$$y = 135$$

Therefore the large bottle contains 35% more than the standard bottle.

REMEMBER

1 Represent the facts on a ratio line.

2 Relate the **original** quantity to 100%.

3 If you are finding a percentage, put the percentage on the top line.

4 Ask yourself if your answer is sensible.

___ Exercise 48

1 ▦ Copy and complete the table. Show all your working.

	Original quantity	Increase	New quantity
a	14 kg	4%	
b	32 m	14%	
c	64 g		73.6 g
d	45 cm³		50.4 cm³

2 ▦ Copy and complete the table. Show all your working.

	Original quantity	Decrease	New quantity
a	28 ml	5%	
b	218 km	21%	
c	£93		£85.56
d	68 mm		55.76 mm

3 ▦ Copy and complete the table. Show all your working.

	Original quantity	Increase	Actual increase
a	£8	12%	
b	31 cm	8%	
c	72 m		3.6 m
d	£15		£2.10

4 ▦ Copy and complete the table. Show all your working.

	Original quantity	Decrease	Actual decrease
a	9.3 kg	22%	
b	7.9 cm²	9%	
c	30 ml		2.7 ml
d	49 km		4.9 km

5 ▦ Ben Nevis is 4400 feet high and Scafell Pike is 3200 feet high. In percentage terms, how much higher is Ben Nevis?

6 🖩 Rupinder, Jenny and Sarah each collect the same kind of sticker and Rupinder has 120 of them.
If Jenny has 30% more than Rupinder, how many has Jenny?
If Sarah has 25% fewer than Rupinder, how many has Sarah?

7 🖩 Arsenal, Chelsea and West Ham all play at home. If there were 35 000 spectators at Arsenal's ground, find:
a The number at Chelsea's ground if there were 15% more than at Arsenal's ground.
b The number at West Ham's ground if there were 18% fewer than at Arsenal's ground.

8 🖩 A new type of men's javelin was introduced in 1986 when the world record was 104.80 m. This javelin could only be thrown about 90% of the distance of the old one. What difference would you expect this type of javelin to have on the world record? Compare your answer to the current world record.

9 🖩 A car has a fuel consumption of 30 mpg. An unloaded roof-rack will reduce this rate of consumption by 5%, a well-loaded roof-rack will reduce it by 10% and a badly loaded roof-rack will reduce it by 15%. Work out, to 2 SF, the mpg in each case.

10 🖩 A nurse earns £8200 a year and a company director earns £110 700 per year. Calculate their new earnings after an 8% increase. Comment.

11 🖩 Interpret these road signs:

What would 100% mean?

12 🖩 A shrimp lays half a million eggs three times a year, but 99.2% of the infant shrimps die before reaching maturity. Find the number which survive per year.

13 🖩 The average adult has 2500 billion red blood cells in his or her body. The bone marrow replaces 8% each day. How many are replaced each day?

14 🖩 A new car costs £10 000. Suppose that inflation is running at 30% per year. Because of this a similar car will cost 30% more a year later. If inflation continues at 30% each year, find the cost of a similar car after **a** 1 year **b** 2 years **c** 3 years **d** 4 years.

15 ▦ The Retail Price Index (RPI) is used to compare prices from one year to the next. From the information in this table, show that prices increased by an average of just over 18% between 1979 and 1980.

Investigate these figures using percentages.

Year	RPI	Year	RPI
1975	100	1983	249
1979	166	1984	256
1980	196	1985	263
1981	219	1986	271
1982	238	1987	280

MASTERMINDERS

16 ▦ The edges of a picture frame are increased by 10%. By what percentage has the area been increased?

17 ▦ The table shows the world record in five events for men and women in 1965, 1975 and 1985. In each case, work out the difference between the men's and women's records, as a percentage of the men's record, correct to 1 DP.

		1965	1975	1985
100 m	Men	10.06 s	9.95 s	9.93 s
	Women	11.23 s	11.07 s	10.76 s
400 m	Men	45.07 s	43.86 s	43.86 s
	Women	51.20 s	49.90 s	47.60 s
1500 m	Men	3 min 35.6 s	3 min 32.2 s	3 min 29.7 s
	Women	4 min 19.0 s	4 min 01.4 s	3 min 52.4 s
High jump	Men	2.28 m	2.30 m	2.41 m
	Women	1.91 m	1.95 m	2.07 m
Long jump	Men	8.35 m	8.90 m	8.90 m
	Women	6.76 m	6.84 m	7.44 m

If all the women's records were 8.4% less than the men's records, estimate the new world record in the women's 1500 m, high jump and long jump.

18 ▦ The ratio of telephones to people in the world is 1 : 8. 0.012% of the world's telephones are in Ethiopia. In Ethiopia 0.2% of the population have telephones. If there are 4000 million people in the world, what is the population of Ethiopia?

___ *Activity 18*

From newspapers, collect information which has been illustrated or explained by using percentages. Comment on your findings.

___ 7.4 Cross-number

Copy and complete the Cross-number. A calculator is **essential**. This is a difficult puzzle, and you may need to ask your teacher for help.

Across

1 A square
4 A square
5 A square
8 Digits sum 35
11 Square root of 39 across
13 A square
14 A square
15 Square of 36 across
17 Square of $\frac{1}{2}$ of 11 across
18 3 digits alike
19 4 across × 33 across
21 A square
22 5 × 5 across
23 All alike except the middle
25 Square of 2 down
27 See 20 down
28 A fourth power
29 18 across plus 31 across
31 A triangular number
33 4 × 36 across +1
34 Digits sum 18
39 A fourth power

36 An odd number
40 A cube

37 All even except 1 and sum 29
41 Twice a square

Down

1 A cube root
4 Digits sum 19
7 A cube
12 Digits sum 30
18 All the same except first which is 1
21 A multiple of 19
26 Square of 18 across
30 A triangular number
35 A cube

2 Square root of 28 across
5 Digits sum 26
9 A cube
14 All the same
22 A square
28 A fourth power of 4 across
32 Digits sum 20, ends in 8
37 A square

3 Sum of 17 and 21 across
6 Sum of 14 across and 33 across
10 A square
16 Sum of digits = 2 down
20 Sum of 17 and 27 across
24 A square
29 Twice 15 across
34 6 times 21 across
38 A cube

___ Revision Exercise 7A

Calculators are **not allowed**.

1 Write $10 \times 10 \times 10$ in index form.

2 Which is larger, 10^6 or $100\,000$?

3 How many times does 10^2 divide into 10^8?

4 Copy and complete: $10^4 \times \square = 10^6$.

5 Which is smaller, 10^{-2} or 0.001?

6 Write in standard form: **a** 391   **b** 0.847.

7 Write as an ordinary number: **a** 5.76×10^3 **b** 1.48×10^{-2}.

8 Lucy is cycling at 34 km/h. She increases her speed by 10%. What is her new speed?

9 Decrease 34 kg by 20%.

10 A train is 200 m long. An extra carriage, of length 40 m, is added. What is the percentage increase in length?

11 The total number of pupils in a school is 280. If the numbers drop to 266, find the percentage decrease.

___ Revision Exercise 7B

Calculators are **not allowed**.

1 Copy and complete: 1000 million $= 10^?$

2 Which is larger: **a** 10^8 or 1 billion   **b** 10^{-4} or 0.001 **c** 10^{-4} or 10^{-5}?

3 Make the following 100 times smaller and write each answer as an ordinary number:
a 10^0 **b** 10^2 **c** 10^{-2}.

4 Write in standard form correct to 2 SF: **a** 2851   **b** 689   **c** 0.0809.

5 Write as an ordinary number: **a** 3.8×10^4 **b** 3.8×10^{-2} **c** 3.8×10^0.

6 A sheet of paper is 10^{-2} mm thick. How many sheets would there be in a pile 10 cm high?

7 Decrease 20 cm by 15%.

8 Increase £25 000 by 2%.

9 In a car park there are 250 cars. If 10 more cars are parked and none leave, find the percentage increase.

10 As a percentage, how much steeper is the steeper hill?
Give your answer to 2 SF.

Basics Test 7

A Calculator

   1 Decrease 95 by 13%.

   2 Change $\frac{119}{37}$ to a decimal, correct to 2 DP.

   3 Work out 0.23×543, to 3 SF.

   4 Solve for x, to 2 SF: $9x = 11$.

   5 $(5.8 - 6.9) \times 44$.

   6 Solve for x: $\frac{9.8}{x} = -2.5$.

B Paper and pencil

   7 Increase £57.80 by 10%.

   8 Solve for y: $39.8 + y = 90.02$.

   9 Simplify $2c^2 \times c^2$.

   10 Simplify $2c^2 - c^2$.

   11 $\frac{7}{8} \div 5\frac{1}{4}$.

   12 Change 0.13 minutes to seconds.

   13 Copy and complete: $\frac{}{120} = \frac{7}{48}$.

   14 Write 0.0765 in standard form.

   15 $2.87 \div (42.38 \times 0.591)$ is nearest to which of the following: 12, 0.12, 0.012?

C Mental

Ten questions will be read out to you. For Questions 16 to 19, select the correct answer from the following list.

16 a 30 cm	**b** 1 m	**c** 1.8 m	**d** 2 m
17 a 2 mm	**b** 2 cm	**c** 2 m	**d** 0.02 km
18 a Your finger	**b** A piece of card	**c** A ruler	**d** Your leg
19 a A drawing pin	**b** A bicycle wheel	**c** A dinner plate	**d** A golf ball

Puzzlers

1 Devise a quick method to add up all the consecutive numbers from 1 to 100 inclusive.

2 A tramp uses six cigar ends to make one whole cigar. How many cigars could he make from 302 cigar ends?

3 The diagram shows sixteen dots in the form of a square. Copy these dots and draw six **straight** lines to pass through all the dots, **without** taking your pencil off the paper.

Coursework: Costing electricity

Electrical power (P) is measured in watts (W) and kilowatts (kW). (1 kW = 1000 W.)

Electricity Boards use 'units of electricity' to work out the charge to their customers. We investigate the cost of running electrical appliances. (Assume the cost of 1 unit is 8p.)

1 A 1 kW appliance which is switched on for 1 hour uses 1 unit of electricity (see the first line of the table). Copy and complete this table.
Use it to explain why $C = PTR$, and that when $R = 8$, $P = \frac{C}{8T}$.

Power (P) in kW	Time (T) in hours	Number of units used	Cost/unit (R) in pence	Total charge (C) in pence
1	1	1	8	8
2	1	2	8	
4	2		8	
2.4		12	7	
	4	20	7	
	5	40		300
P	2		8	
6	T		R	
P	T		R	

2 Twelve appliances are listed in the table below. Copy it and complete the second column. (Put 1 against the appliance which you think uses most electricity, 2 against the next, etc.)

Appliance	Descending order of power		Time (T)	Cost (C)	Power (kW)
	Guess	Actual			
Electric fire			3 hours	48p	
Television			2.8 hours	6.16p	
Microwave oven			0.5 hour	2p	
Ceiling bulb			2 days	38.4p	
Shower			2.5 hours	£1.60	
Kettle			mins	0.64p	2.4
Refrigerator			1 day	28.8p	
Oven			1 year	£	3
Table lamp			100 years	£	0.06
Freezer			years	£1331.52	0.19
Small radio			6 hours 12 mins	0.496p	
10 mm drill			36 seconds	0.032p	

a Use the formula $P = \frac{C}{8T}$ to help complete the table. (Remember T is in hours, C is in pence and P is in kilowatts. Take 365 days in a year.)

b Comment on how your guesses matched the actual power of each appliance.

EXTENSION

3 **Investigate** how much more economic it is to use a microwave rather than a conventional oven.

8 STATISTICS AND PROBABILITY

8.1 Basic principles

Means (averages)

The numbers used to calculate a mean are the total of each quantity used. For example,

$$\text{Mean goals scored per match} = \frac{\text{TOTAL number of goals scored}}{\text{TOTAL number of matches}}$$

$$\text{Mean speed in metres per second} = \frac{\text{TOTAL distance in metres}}{\text{TOTAL time in seconds}}$$

(Remember that 'per' means 'divide by'.)

■ *EXAMPLE 1*

The table shows the number of goals scored by a team in each of twelve hockey matches. Find the mean number of goals scored per match.

Number of goals scored	0	1	2	3	4
Number of matches in which these number of goals were scored	1	2	4	3	2

[W]   Mean number of goals scored per match

$$= \frac{\text{TOTAL number of goals scored}}{\text{TOTAL number of matches}}$$

[W] $= \dfrac{(0 \times 1) + (1 \times 2) + (2 \times 4) + (3 \times 3) + (4 \times 2)}{12} = \dfrac{27}{12}$

[A] $= 2.25$

Probability

Probability is used to predict the likelihood of an event happening. If you throw an ordinary die, each of the six faces is equally likely to appear. Therefore the probability of, say, throwing a five, is 1/6, because there is only one five on the die but it has six faces.

An event which is determined by chance is called a 'random' event. In other words, all the possible outcomes are equally likely to occur.

REMEMBER

$$\text{Probability of an event happening} = \frac{\text{Number of desired outcomes}}{\text{Number of possible outcomes}}$$

■ EXAMPLE 2

A special die has its faces marked with the numbers, 1, 3, 3, 4, 4, 4. Find the probability of throwing
a a 3 **b** not a 4.

a [W] Probability of a 3

　[W] $= \dfrac{2}{6}$ ◁ Number of desired outcomes

　　　　　　◁ Number of possible outcomes

　[A] $= \frac{1}{3}$

b [W] Probability of not a 4

　[W] $= \dfrac{3}{6}$ ◁ Number of desired outcomes

　　　　　　◁ Number of possible outcomes

　[A] $= \frac{1}{2}$

■ EXAMPLE 3

There are 20 coloured beads in a box. 12 are black, 6 are blue and 2 are red. If a bead is selected
at random, what is the probability that it is a blue?

　[W] Probability that it is a blue

　[W] $= \dfrac{6}{20}$

　[A] $= \frac{3}{10}$

> **REMEMBER**
>
> When collecting data, it is often useful to use 'tally marks':
>
> 5 is written ‖‖‖   8 is written ‖‖‖ ‖‖‖

▬ Bar charts

A bar chart is one way of representing data. Look carefully at Example 4.

■ EXAMPLE 4

Draw a bar chart to represent the data given in Example 1. Find the probability that if one of the
results were chosen at random, the team had scored more than 2 goals.

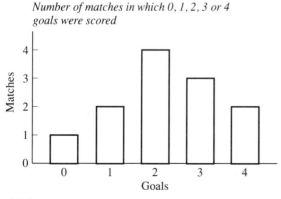

*Number of matches in which 0, 1, 2, 3 or 4
goals were scored*

　[W] Probability of more than 2 goals

　[W] $= \dfrac{3+2}{12}$

　[A] $= \frac{5}{12}$

—— Exercise 49

1 A model train travels 56 m in 23 seconds and then 94 m in 27 seconds. Find its mean speed, for the whole journey, in metres per second.

2 A car travels 51 miles in 48 minutes and then 21 miles in 24 minutes. Find its mean speed, for the whole journey, in miles per hour.

3 In an essay, the number of spelling mistakes are counted in each paragraph. The number of lines and spelling mistakes, in two paragraphs, are shown below.

	1st paragraph	*2nd paragraph*
Number of lines	18	22
Number of mistakes	4	12

Find the mean number of spelling mistakes per line.

4 Here are the results of counting the daisies in two different areas of a lawn.

Area of lawn (m²)	24	11
Number of daisies	67	38

Find the mean number of daisies per square metre.

5 A special die has its faces marked with the numbers 2, 4, 6, 7, 8, 9. Find the probability of throwing **a** a 6 **b** an odd **c** an even.
Comment on the sum of your last two answers.

6 A special die has its faces marked with the numbers 2, 2, 3, 4, 5, 5. Find the probability of throwing **a** a 2 **b** a prime **c** not a prime.
Comment on the sum of your last two answers.

7 A bag contains one blue, two pink and four green marbles. If a marble is selected at random, work out the probability that it is **a** a pink **b** a blue **c** not a green.

8 A card is randomly selected from a pack of 52 playing cards. Find the probability of obtaining **a** a red card **b** a Queen **c** not a spade.

9 Margaret decides to keep a record of the vegetables served for lunch on each of the 84 days of one term. Her findings were:

Beans   36 days   Cabbage   27 days
Peas   18 days   Salad   3 days

a Draw a bar chart to represent the data.

b Margaret's parents had lunch in school on one day in the term. What was the probability that peas were **not** on the menu?

10 Five European football teams played together in the same qualifying group for the World Cup. The results were:

Norway 2 Sweden 3   Norway 3 Iceland 1
Sweden 4 Finland 2   Sweden 0 Denmark 2
Iceland 1 Sweden 2   Iceland 2, Finland 1
Denmark 0 Iceland 2   Denmark 3 Norway 3
Finland 2 Norway 2   Finland 3 Denmark 0

a Draw a bar chart to show the number of goals scored by each country.
b Find, for each country, the mean number of goals scored per match.

11 The bar chart shows how many passengers travelled from Exeter to Barnstaple by each of the six available trains on a certain day.

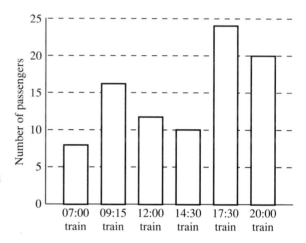

Exeter station: Train departures to Barnstaple	
07:00	14:30
09:15	17:30
12:00	20:00

Find from the chart:
a The total number of passengers carried on that particular day.
b The mean number of passengers per train.
c The total collected in fares if the fare is £7.20 before 09:30 and £6.00 after that.
d The mean fare paid per passenger.

8.2 Pie charts

A pie chart is a way of representing data as the sectors making up a circle – the slices of the 'pie'. We describe each sector by its angle, say, 30°, 65°; so the whole 'pie' is 360°. Look at the following examples.

■ EXAMPLE 1

The table shows how many cars used a ferry on each day of a certain week.

Draw a pie chart to display this information.

	Day of the week	Number of cars
a	Monday	12
b	Tuesday	8
c	Wednesday	4
d	Thursday	8
e	Friday	12
f	Saturday	16
g	Sunday	20

The 'sector' angle for each day is proportional to the number of cars which used the ferry on each day. The sector angle is worked out using the Unitary Method (see page 49). The 'total' angle – 360° – represents the total number of cars, that is, 80 cars.

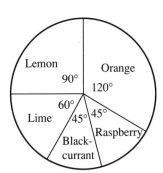

Question quantity   *Answer quantity*

80 cars are represented by   360°

1 car is represented by $\frac{360}{80}$ = 4.5°

a   12 cars are represented by   4.5 × 12   = 54°
b   8 cars are represented by   4.5 × 8   = 36°
c   4 cars are represented by   4.5 × 4   = 18°
d   8 cars are represented by   4.5 × 8   = 36°
e   12 cars are represented by   4.5 × 12   = 54°
f   16 cars are represented by   4.5 × 16   = 72°
g   20 cars are represented by   4.5 × 20   = 90°

Notice that the total of all the angles is 360°.
A protractor and pair of compasses are needed to draw the pie chart.

■ EXAMPLE 2

Packets of fruit-flavoured sweets always contain a total of 48 sweets, of five different flavours. The pie chart shows how many sweets of each flavour are included in each packet, as a fraction of the total.
Find the number of sweets of each flavour per packet.

The number of sweets of a given flavour is proportional to the sector angle. The quantity is worked out using the Unitary Method. The total number of sweets is represented by the angle of 360°.

        Question quantity   *Answer quantity*
        360° represents   48 sweets
        1° represents $\frac{48}{360}$ = $\frac{2}{15}$ sweets

Orange   120° represents $\frac{2}{15}$ × 120   = 16 sweets

Lemon   90° represents $\frac{2}{15}$ × 90   = 12 sweets

Lime   60° represents $\frac{2}{15}$ × 60   = 8 sweets

Blackcurrant   45° represents $\frac{2}{15}$ × 45   = 6 sweets

Raspberry   45° represents $\frac{2}{15}$ × 45   = 6 sweets

Notice that the total number of sweets is 48.

REMEMBER

1 Work out each angle, using the Unitary Method, from the information given.

2 Label each sector and include the angle.

3 Check that the sum of all the angles is 360°.

129

___ Exercise 50

1 One year 36 000 people travelled from Scotland to Wembley Stadium to see an international football match. The pie chart shows how they travelled. Find the number who travelled by each of the four modes of transport.

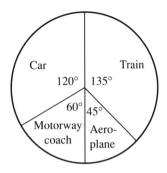

2 At a London school 120 boys were asked which county cricket team they supported. They answered as follows:

40 supported Middlesex   35 supported Surrey
25 supported Kent   20 supported Essex

Display these details on a pie chart.

3 120 teenagers from the London area were asked which football team they supported. Their answers were as follows:

36 supported Arsenal   30 supported Tottenham Hotspur
24 supported Chelsea   18 supported West Ham United
12 supported Queen's Park Rangers

Display these details on a pie chart.

4 a A vending machine sells crisps of six different flavours, and on one particular day 240 packets were sold. Find from the pie chart how many packets of each flavour were sold.

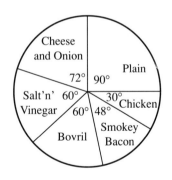

b The machine accepts 5p, 10p and 20p coins and does not give change. If 450 coins were paid into the machine by the end of the day, find from the pie chart (i) the number of coins of each kind that were paid in (ii) the total amount of money collected (iii) the price of one packet of crisps.

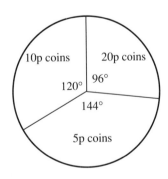

MASTERMINDERS

5 **a** A train leaves Liverpool Street Station in London and calls at Chelmsford, Colchester, Ipswich and Norwich. If 420 people board the train in London, find from the pie chart how many are bound for each of the four destinations.

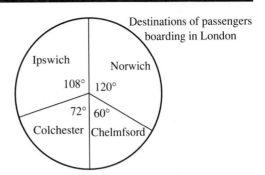

Destinations of passengers boarding in London

b After leaving London, the train only picks up passengers who are travelling to Norwich. If there are 300 people on the train after it has left Ipswich, find from the pie chart the number of passengers who joined the train at each of the four boarding points.

c By using your answers to parts **a** and **b**, copy and complete this table showing the number of passengers on the train.

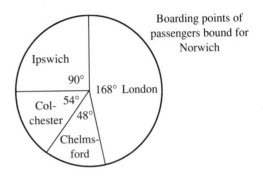

Boarding points of passengers bound for Norwich

Section of journey	No. of passengers
London to Chelmsford	420
Chelmsford to Colchester	
Colchester to Ipswich	
Ipswich to Norwich	300

6 The pie charts below show the relative sizes of the Earth's principal oceans and continents.

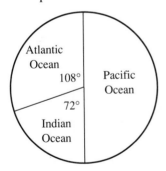
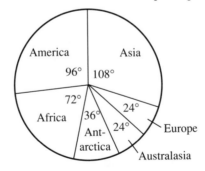

Given that the surface area of the Earth is 500 000 000 square kilometres and that the ratio of sea area to land area is 7 : 3, estimate the area of each of the three principal oceans and each of the six continents.

Comment on whether you think the two pie charts should have been drawn to the same size.

___ *Activity 19*

From newspapers, collect examples of pie charts and comment on the information displayed.

— 8.3 Probability

— Notation

There is a special way of writing down probabilities. For example, suppose you are tossing a coin. Then the probability of throwing 'heads' is written p(heads), and 'tails' is p(tails). In general:

> **NOTE**
>
> $p(A)$ means the probability of event A happening.

— *Activity 20*

You should work in pairs for this Activity. Each pair is given the following six playing cards:

- Any one picture card (not an Ace)
- Any three black numbered cards (not an Ace)
- Any two red numbered cards (not an Ace)

Shuffle the cards and place them face down on a desk. Select one card and note its type on a table, using tally marks.

You need a total of 300 choices from the whole class. Gather together the results of the whole class on a table like this:

Type of card	Total
Picture Red numbered Black numbered	
	300

1   **Use the results from the whole class** to work out the probability of selecting each of the three types of card. (Your answers are called the 'experimental probability' because they have been worked out from experimental results.)

2   Now work out the 'theoretical probability' of selecting each type of card. (Your answers are what you would **expect** the results of your experiment to be.)

3   Compare your two sets of answers. Explain why you would not expect the experimental results to be exactly the same as the theoretical results.

4 Using the six cards, explain the following:

$$p(\text{Selecting an Ace}) = \frac{0}{6} = 0$$

5 Now work out the sum of the three theoretical probabilities obtained in part 2. Your result should show that if an event is bound to occur, the probability of that event happening is 1.

6 Copy this scale across your page.

On it, mark the probability of selecting:

a An Ace.
b A picture card.
c A black numbered card.
d A red numbered card.
e Either a picture card, a red numbered card or a black numbered card.

> **REMEMBER**
>
> All probabilities must be less than or equal to 1 but greater than or equal to 0.

Activity 21

1 If a drawing pin is dropped, guess the probability of it landing

2 Drop a drawing pin 50 times and record its landing position, on a suitable table, using tally marks. Work out the experimental probability of each landing position. How does your guess compare with your results?

Activity 22

1 If two dice are thrown, guess the probability that the same number will appear on both dice.

2 Throw two dice 60 times and record the number of times the same number appears on both dice. Work out the experimental probability of this event happening. How does your guess compare with your results?

133

___ Exercise 51

1   A card is randomly selected from a pack of 52 playing cards. Work out the probability that it is
    a a club   **b** an Ace   **c** not a red card.

2   An ordinary die is thrown. Work out the probability of obtaining **a** a 6   **b** a 1 or 2   **c** not a 6.

3   In the middle of winter a school's central heating system has broken down on 24 days in a
    period of five weeks. What is the probability that it will go wrong tomorrow?

4   The probability a car will get a puncture in 30 000 miles is 4/11. What is the probability of a
    puncture-free 30 000 miles?

5   In a raffle 365 tickets are sold. What is the probability that you will win first prize if you have
    bought 15 tickets?

6   Michael records the first bird he sees on 50 successive days.

Great tit

卌 卌

Sparrow

卌 卌 卌

Coal tit

卌 I

Wren

II

Blue tit

卌 卌 III

Wagtail

IIII

What is the probability that the first bird he sees tomorrow is not a sparrow?

7   A bag of sweets contains five mints, six chocolates and seven toffees. If one sweet is taken at
    random, what is the probability that it is **a** a chocolate   **b** a mint   **c** not a toffee?

MASTERMINDER

8   Two ordinary dice are thrown 60 times. What is the probability that the same number appears
    on both dice? Compare your answer with your answers in Activity 22.

Revision Exercise 8A

1 In a survey, 60 pupils were asked which of four subjects they liked best. The results were:
Science 15   Maths 30   English 10   French 5
Display these facts on a pie chart.

2 In one day 4800 vehicles pass a certain road junction. The pie chart shows the types of vehicle. Find the number of each type of vehicle which pass the road junction.

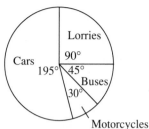

3 In two different flower beds, the number of tulip bulbs is counted. The results are:

Area of flower bed (m^2)	4.4	6.6
Number of tulip bulbs	24	31

Find the mean number of bulbs per square metre.

4 A card is randomly selected from an ordinary pack of 52 playing cards. Find the probability of selecting **a** a black card   **b** a King   **c** not a heart.

5 In a raffle 2800 tickets are sold. What is the probability that you will win first prize if you have bought **a** 20 tickets   **b** 200 tickets   **c** 400 tickets?

Revision Exercise 8B

1 The table shows the number of cars of different makes in a car park.

Make	Fiat	Ford	Nissan	Rover	Citroën
Number	5	50	30	18	17

Represent this information on a pie chart.

2 The pie chart shows the grades, A, B, C and D obtained in an examination.
a What percentage obtained a grade C?
b If a fifth of the total obtained a grade A, work out the size of angles x and y.

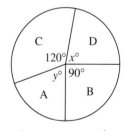

3 A drawing office clerk has a new pencil which is 16 cm long. After seven weeks, with five working days in a week, he finds that the pencil is only 9 cm long. Find:
a The mean rate at which the pencil length decreases per day.
b The time for which he uses the pencil if he throws it away when it is only 4 cm long.

4 One letter is selected at random from the word 'ACCOMMODATING'. Find the probability of selecting: **a** a C   **b** a D   **c** a vowel   **d** an M or O.

5 A bag contains four red balls, five blue balls and six green balls. If one ball is selected at random, what is the probability that it is **a** a green ball   **b** a red ball   **c** a yellow ball   **d** either a red ball or a blue ball.

Basics Test 8

A Calculator

1 $\frac{4.6 \times 2.9}{6.4 \times 9.2}$ to 2 SF

2 Solve for y: $13y = 221$.

3 Which is smallest? $\frac{12}{13}$, 0.93, $\frac{13}{15}$.

4 Find the mean of: $\frac{1}{8}$, 0.13, 0.04, 1.901.

5 Change $2\frac{14}{17}$ to a decimal correct to 3 SF.

6 Solve for x: $\frac{43.7}{x} = 1.9$

B Paper and pencil

7 What percentage of 80 is 49?

8 $10^3 \times 0.01$

9 100×10^{-2}

10 Simplify $3a \times 4b$.

11 Solve for c: $3.895 = 2.01 - c$.

12 $10^{-2} \div \frac{1}{1000}$

13 $\sqrt{1.69}$

14 The mass of a large loaf of bread is d grams. Write down the total mass of n similar loaves in kilograms.

15 A number of 10p pieces are placed in a straight line with no gaps. If the length of the line is 25 m, the total value of all the coins is approximately **a** £25 **b** £100 **c** £500 **d** £1000 **e** £5000?

C Mental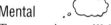

Ten questions will be read out to you.

You will need the following information for Questions 16 to 20.

   1 pint of beer cost £1.60   1 glass of lemonade costs 80p

   1 glass of cider costs 90p   1 packet of crisps costs 21p

Puzzlers

1 Two cats together catch sixty mice. If Percy catches three mice for every two that Hannibal catches, how many does Percy catch?

2 How many positive whole numbers have their square roots between 100 and 101?

3 A cell X divides into two separate cells Y and Z. This process is repeated another eleven times, making twelve times in all. The first two divisions, making a total of seven cells, are shown below.

If no cell dies, find the total number of cells after twelve divisions.

Coursework: Memory investigation

It is an advantage to have a good memory. How good is yours? In this Coursework your memory will be tested, together with the others in your class. You will then use mathematics to analyse the results.

1 You will be given two minutes to learn the items on the following Shopping List **in the given order**. You must not write anything down.

SHOPPING LIST			
1 FISH	6 PEANUTS	11 COFFEE	16 PEARS
2 ROLLS	7 ONIONS	12 ORANGES	17 SPAGHETTI
3 LETTUCE	8 WINE	13 BOVRIL	18 PEAS
4 CHOCOLATE	9 KETCHUP	14 LEEKS	19 SALAD CREAM
5 DOG FOOD	10 PEPPER	15 TEA	20 LOLLIPOP

You will then be given two minutes to write down, **in the given order**, all the items you can remember from the list. (This does not mean you have to write item 1 first, item 2 second, etc.) Make a note of how many you get right.

2 Grades, A, B, C, D and E are given to the marks as shown on the following table. Copy this table and complete it, showing all the results from your class.

Grade	A	B	C	D	E
Range of marks	20–15	14–12	11–9	8–6	5–0
Number of pupils obtaining the grade					

3 Draw a pie chart and a bar chart to illustrate the results. Comment on whether you think it is better to use a pie chart or a bar chart. (Work out each angle of the pie chart to the nearest degree.)

4 If a pupil from your class is selected at random, find the probability that he or she gained a grade A or B in the test.

EXTENSION

5 **Investigate** the following statement: 'Those with good memories are also good at French'.

9 GRAPHS II

9.1 Travel graphs

Journeys can be illustrated on a graph by plotting the distance travelled against the time taken. These graphs are called 'travel graphs'. The time is always plotted along the horizontal axis.

■ *EXAMPLE 1*

The graph shows details of two journeys, one by Paul, who travels from Amford to Bester, and the other by Mark, who travels from Bester to Amford.

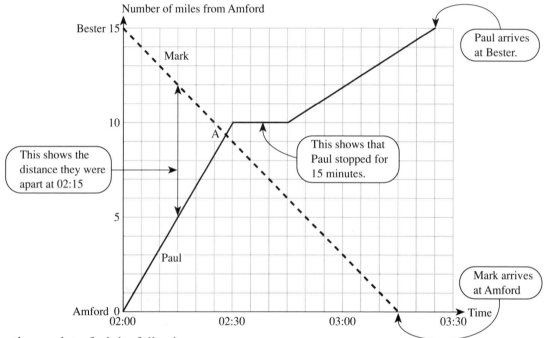

Use the graph to find the following:

a   The time Mark arrived at Amford.
b   For how long Paul stopped during his journey.
c   How far apart were they at 02:15.
d   Paul's mean speed after his stop.
e   Mark's mean speed.
f   Where and when they passed each other.

a   Mark arrived at Amford at 03:15.
b   Paul stopped for 15 minutes.
c   Paul and Mark were 7 miles apart at 02:15.
d   Paul's mean speed, after his stop = $5 \div \frac{2}{3} = 7.5$ miles/h. (40 minutes = $\frac{2}{3}$ hour.)
e   Mark's mean speed = $15 \div 1.25 = 12$ miles/h.
f   They passed each other at about 02:28 at the point marked 'A', about 9.4 miles from Amford.

138

REMEMBER

When using a graph:

● Work out the scale used on both axes.

● A steeper slope on a travel graph represents a faster speed.

● Always use words to explain your answers.

When drawing a graph:

● Time is always represented on the horizontal axis.

● Label both axes and all lines carefully.

Activity 23

This two-track railway line connects station A to station E, with stations B, C and D between.

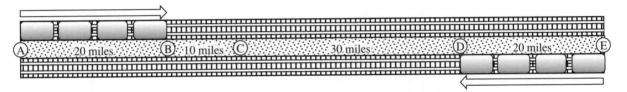

The company which owns the line plans to run ten trains between 09:00 and 11:00. Their **proposed** plans are shown on the travel graph below.

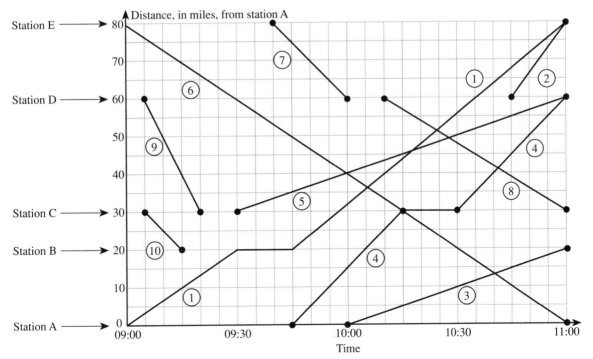

1 Copy the partially completed time-tables shown below. Use the details on the travel graph (page 139) to help complete them. *Note*: 'a' means arrive, 'd' means depart.

Distance from A (miles)	Station	Train number				
		1	2	3	4	5
0	A	09 00	–			
20	B a	09 30	–			
	B d	09 45	–			
30	C a	–	–			
	C d	–	–			
60	D a	–	–			
	D d	–	10 45			
80	E	11 00	11 00			
Mean speed (miles per hour)		40	80			

Distance from E (miles)	Station	Train number				
		6	7	8	9	10
0	E	09 00				
20	D a	–				
	D d	–				
50	C a	–				
	C d	–				
60	B a	–				
	B d	–				
80	A	11 00				
Mean speed (miles per hour)						

2 Between what times are there the most trains actually moving?
3 Describe, in detail, a journey on Train 4.

___ Exercise 52

1 The graph shows the journeys of a bus and a van, along the same road, between Darchester and Brodport.
   a For how long was the bus stationary during the journey?
   b At what speed was the van travelling?
   c Between what times was the bus travelling fastest?
   d How far apart were the van and bus at 13:20?
   e Approximately, where and when did the two vehicles meet?

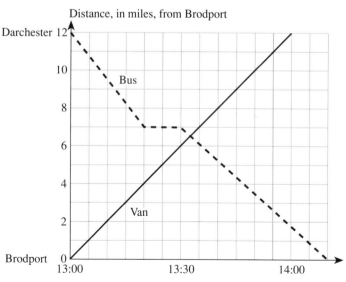

2 The graph shows how a cyclist and a motorist travelled between the towns of Bexeter and Bodhampton.

a For how long was the motorist stationary during the journey?

b What was the motorist's speed between 16:00 and 16:30?

c About how far from Bexeter did the motorist meet the cyclist?

d What was the motorist's mean speed for the whole journey?

e What was the approximate speed of the cyclist at 17:30?

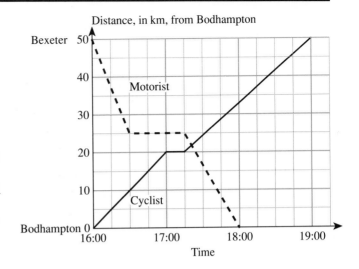

3 The graph shows the journeys of Mary and Marion who went on a cycling trip.

a For how long did Mary stop?

b At what time did Marion start?

c How far did they each cycle?

d What was Marion's mean speed?

e About how far apart were they at 11:40?

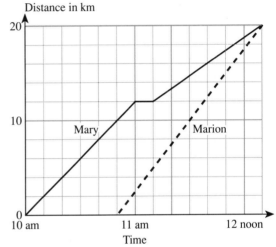

4 The graph shows the journeys of two express Coaches A and B, travelling on the motorway from Edingo to Glasburgh.

a Where do you think the motorway service area is?

b At what times did Coach A overtake Coach B?

c How fast was Coach A travelling at 14:45?

d What was the mean speed of Coach B?

e Approximately, when did Coach A arrive in Glasburgh?

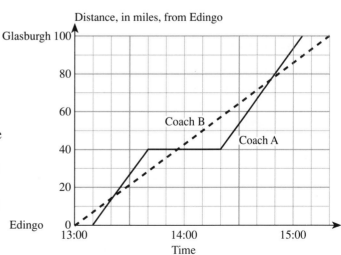

141

5 The line drawn on the graph represents a speed of 30 km/h.

Copy the graph and draw lines from A to represent each of the following speeds. Label each line with the speed it represents.
a 50 km/h
b 20 km/h
c 40 km/h
d 5 km/h.

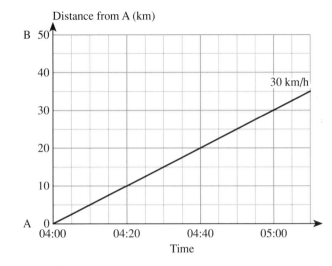

6 The line drawn on the graph represents a speed of 25 miles/h.

Copy the graph and draw lines from B to represent each of the following speeds. Label each line with the speed it represents.
a 20 miles/h
b 10 miles/h
c 30 miles/h
d 50 miles/h.

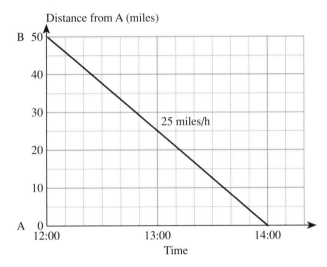

7 The line drawn on the graph represents a speed of 4 m/s.

Copy the graph and draw lines from A to represent each of the following speeds. Label each line with the speed it represents.
a 8 m/s
b 10 m/s
c 3 m/s
d 20 m/s.

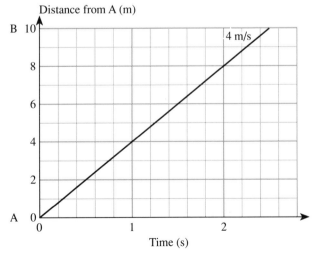

8 The line drawn on the graph represents a speed of 5 m/s.

Copy the graph and draw lines from B to represent each of the following speeds. Label each line with the speed it represents.

a 2 m/s
b 1 m/s
c 10 m/s
d 25 m/s.

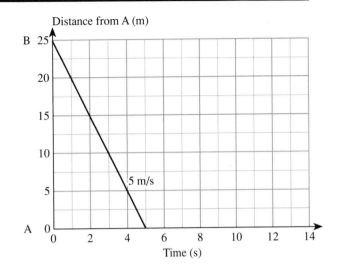

9 The graph shows a car journey made by Mrs Smith who takes her daughter to school and returns home. Copy this graph.

a Work out the car's mean speed
(i) to school   (ii) from school.
b A minibus leaves the school at 08:15 and travels along the same road to pass Mrs Smith's house at 09:20. On your graph draw the line to represent this journey.
Where and when did the car and the minibus pass each other?

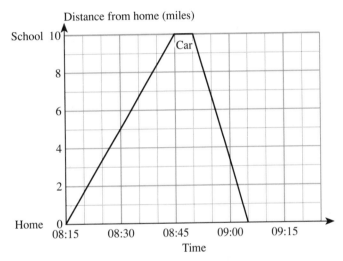

10 The graph shows the journeys of Susan and Fiona who cycle from their homes to meet at a picnic park. Copy this graph.

After staying at the picnic park for 15 minutes, Fiona cycles home at 8 miles/h and Susan cycles home at 10 miles/h.
a Represent these facts on your graph.
b At what time did each arrive home?
c Excluding the stop at the picnic park, work out the mean speed for each girl.

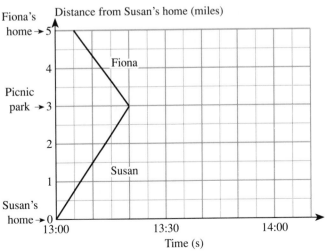

11 Peter cycles to his grandmother's house which is 18 km away from where he lives. On his way back he calls at his uncle's house. The travel graph shows his journey.

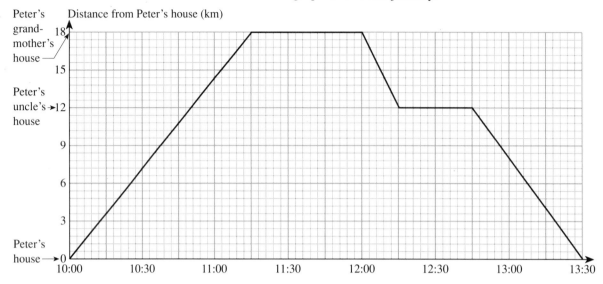

    a How long did Peter stay at (i) his grandmother's house   (ii) his uncle's house?

    c What was Peter's speed (i) between his own house and his Grandmother's house   (ii) between 12:00 and 12:15   (iii) between his uncle's house and his own house?

12 Anne walks to Jane's house and then they walk together to a fair. They are both given a lift in a car back to Anne's house after they have visited the fair.

    a How long did they spend at the fair?

    b What was the speed of
      (i) Anne from 14:00 to 14:30.
      (ii) Anne and Jane when they walked to the fair.
      (iii) Their car journey?

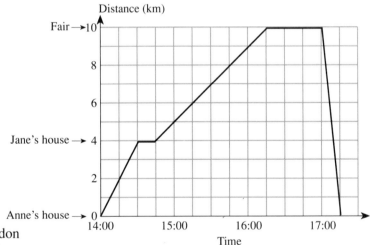

13 A train makes a journey from London to Aberdeen, as shown in the table. Using a horizontal scale of 2 cm to 1 hour, and a vertical scale of 1 cm to 50 km, draw a graph which shows the distance in terms of time.

    a Find the mean speed of the train for each of the six stages of the journey.

    b Find the overall mean speed from London to Aberdeen.

Location	Distance from London (km)	Time
London (Kings X)	0	08:00
Huntingdon	90	08:30
York	300	11:30
Newcastle	430	12:30
Edinburgh	630	14:30
Dundee	720	16:00
Aberdeen	840	18:30

MASTERMINDERS

14 Ancaster, Bancaster and Cancaster are towns on a motorway.

At 14:00 there is a bank robbery at Bancaster and the gang immediately drive on the motorway, at 50 miles/h, towards Cancaster. At 14:15 the police at Ancaster are alerted and immediately drive at 100 miles/h to Bancaster. They spend half an hour at the scene of the crime and then drive towards Cancaster at 100 miles/h in pursuit of the robbers.

a Using a scale of 2 cm to 50 miles and 2 cm to 30 minutes, draw a travel graph to show these events.

b Use your graph to find how far from Cancaster the robbers are when the police catch up with them.

15 The diagram represents a street which is 800 m long.

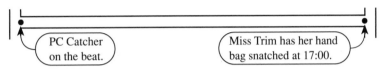

On snatching Miss Trim's handbag, the thief runs up the street at 200 m/minute. One minute after the robbery PC Catcher runs down the street towards the thief at 300 m/minute.

a Choose suitable scales and draw a travel graph to illustrate these events.

b Use your graph to find (i) how far PC Catcher has to run before catching the thief   (ii) for how long the thief is running before being caught.

___ 9.2 Information graphs

This section covers some more uses – and misuses – of graphs.

___ Exercise 53

1 Rain water from a small garage roof is collected in a butt. The graphs in this question refer to the depth of water in the butt.

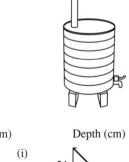

a What is likely to have caused the reduction in the depth of the water as represented in each graph?

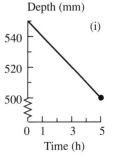

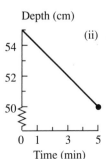

b Which graph is most likely to represent the butt filling up with rain from the garage roof?

c Make up a story about each of the these graphs.

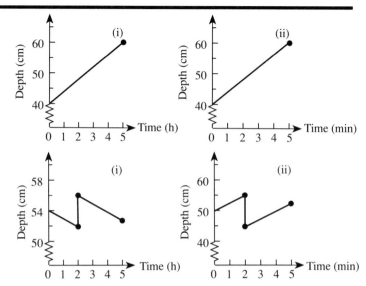

2 This graph and headline were published in a national newspaper. Why are they misleading?

Dramatic Fall in Unemployment

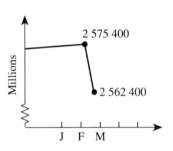

2 575 400

2 562 400

J F M

MASTERMINDER

3 Make up a story about this graph.

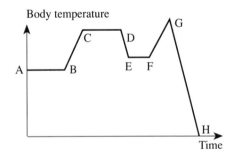

4 Make up a story about this graph.

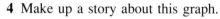
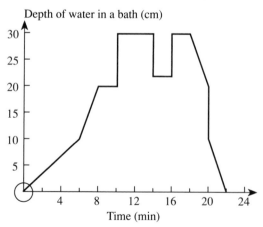

___ *Activity 24*

Collect your own line graphs from newspapers and magazines and write a brief comment about each. Try to find at least one which could be misleading.

146

Revision Exercise 9A

1   The graph shows the journeys of a car
    and a motor-cycle, along the same road
    between Xford and Yford.

    a At what speed was the car travelling?
    b What was the total journey time of
      the motor-cycle?
    c For how long was the motor-cycle
      stationary during the journey?
    d When did the two vehicles pass each
      other?
    e At what speed was the motor-cycle
      travelling at (i) 12:15   (ii) 12:57?
    f How far apart were the vehicles at
      12:40?

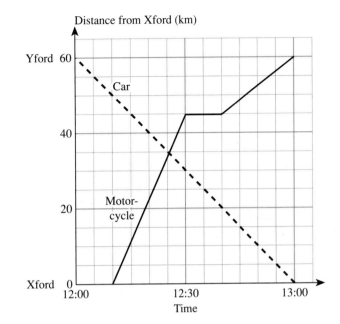

2   The graph shows details of the journey
    of a bus travelling from Aford towards
    Bford. Copy this graph.

    a Describe, in as much detail as
      possible, the bus's journey.
    b A car leaves Bford at 08:00 and
      travels towards Aford at 50 miles/h.
      On your graph represent the details
      of the car's journey.
    c When, and where, did the bus pass
      the car?
    d Approximately, how far apart are the
      two vehicles at 08:10?

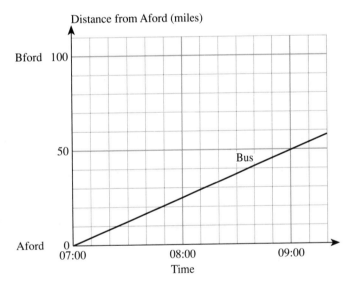

147

▬ Revision Exercise 9B

1 The diagram shows John's route to work from his home.

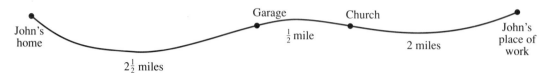

John leaves home on his motor-cycle at 08:00. Five minutes later his motor-cycle breaks down by the church. He takes 15 minutes to push it back to the garage. After repairs, which take 5 minutes, he sets off for work at 36 miles/h.

a Using a scale of 2 cm to 5 minutes and 2 cm to 1 mile, draw a travel graph to represent John's journey to work.

b Estimate from your graph John's arrival time at work.

2 Missile A is fired at a target 200 km away. The target is defended by Missile B (an anti-missile missile) which can be positioned anywhere along the line drawn below. (You should assume that both missiles travel in a horizontal straight line towards each other and that there is no limit to how far Missile B can travel.)

Speed of Missile A = 40 km/min
Speed of Missile B = 60 km/min

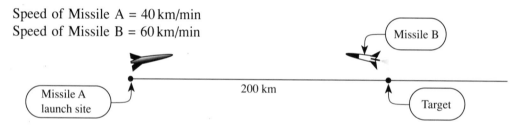

a Using a scale of 1 cm to 50 km, up to 500 km, and 2 cm to 1 minute, up to 5 minutes, draw a travel graph to represent Missile A's journey.

b On your graph draw a line to represent the path of Missile B, if it is fired from the target area immediately Missile A is fired. Use your graph to work out:

(i) How far Missile B travels before it hits Missile A.

(ii) For how long Missile B is in flight before it hits Missile A.

c Investigate where Missile B can be positioned if it has to be fired at least a minute before it hits Missile A.

___ Aural Test 1

Twenty questions will be read out to you. You may do any workings on a piece of paper. You will need the following information to answer Questions 11 to 20.

11 and **12**

 Thousands 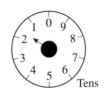 Hundreds  Tens   Units

13   **a** 1280   **b** 6900   **c** 7482   **d** 69 000   **e** 6536

14   **a** $\frac{1}{4}$ tonne   **b** 1 tonne   **c** $1\frac{3}{4}$ tonnes   **d** 2 tonnes   **e** 5 tonnes

15 and **16**

17 to **20**

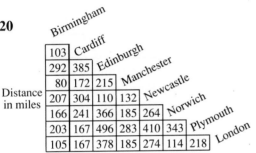

___ Puzzlers

1   Arrange six matches as shown. By adding five more matches to the arrangement, make nine.

2   A polygon has n sides. How many diagonals does it have?

3   The diagram shows a sheet of twelve postage stamps. How many ways can four stamps be torn off so that all four remain joined together? (Hint: be methodical as there are over fifty different ways. Draw diagrams to illustrate your answer.)

1	2	3	4
5	6	7	8
9	10	11	12

Coursework: Animal speed records

In this Coursework, we explore the relative speeds of the fastest bird (Spine-tailed Swift), the fastest fish (Sailfish), the fastest racehorse, the fastest human – and your fastest time to run 100 metres.

The graph on the right converts the time taken to travel 100 m into the mean speed in mph.

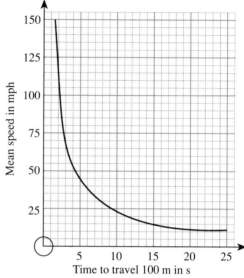

1 The table below shows the time it would take each creature to travel 25 miles at its record-breaking speed. (You should assume that each could maintain its speed for this distance.)

Creature	Spine-tailed Swift	Sailfish	Racehorse	Human
Time (min)	14	22	34	53

Draw a graph using a horizontal scale of 2 cm to 10 minutes (from 0 minutes to 30 minutes) and a vertical scale of 2 cm to 5 miles (from 0 miles to 30 miles). Plot the above details by drawing four separate straight lines. Also draw a straight line to represent your own mean speed over the 100 m.

2 Copy and complete the following table by using your graph and the conversion graph at the top of this page.

Creature	Distance travelled in 15 minutes (miles)	Mean speed (miles per hour)	Time to travel 100 m (seconds)
Spine-tailed swift Sailfish Racehorse Human Yourself			

EXTENSION

3 a An object is moving at a constant speed of v miles/h. Show that its approximate time T, in seconds, to travel 100 m is given by the equation:

$$T \approx \frac{224}{v} \quad (1 \text{ mile} \approx 1610 \text{ m})$$

  b Richard Noble, in his record-breaking 'Thrust 2', took 0.35 seconds to travel 100 m. Estimate his speed in miles/h.

10 TRANSFORMATIONS

10.1 Basic algebraic graphs

A transformation is a change of form. In Mathematics, the three basic transformations are reflection, rotation and translation. But before you learn about these, you must be able to define certain straight lines on a graph.

Activity 25

1 In Graph A, all the co-ordinates which are points on the line marked (a) have an x-value of 2; the line is the graph of $x = 2$.

   Write down the co-ordinate of each point on the line marked (b) and explain why the line is the graph of $y = 3$. Then write down the equations of the lines marked (c), (d), the x-axis and the y-axis.

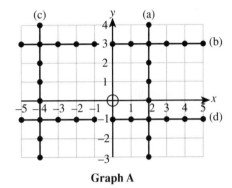

Graph A

2 In Graph B, all the co-ordinates which give points on the line marked (e), have the x-value equal to the y-value: the line is the graph of $y = x$.

   Use Graph B to explain why the line marked (f) is the graph of $y = -x$, or $y + x = 0$.

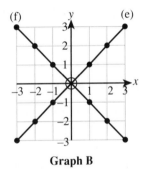

Graph B

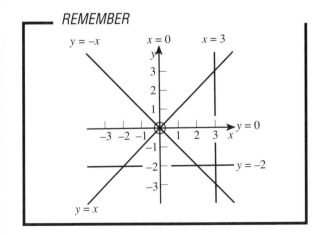

REMEMBER

Exercise 54

1 Write down the equation of the line which is represented by each side of the following figures.

a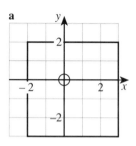
b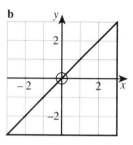
c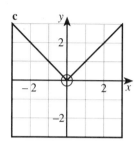
d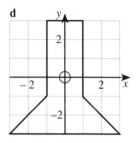

2 Write down the equations of each of three lines which pass through the points: **a** (2, 2) **b** (3, −3) **c** (−15, −15) **d** (−a, a)

MASTERMINDER

3 A (0, −10) and C (0, −30) are two opposite vertices of a rhombus. Write down the equation of each of the two lines of symmetry.

10.2 Reflections

> **NOTE**
>
> Reflection is defined by the mirror line.
>
> Use the folding method to find the mirror line.

Activity 26

On graph paper, plot the points A (−4, 2) and B (−2, 5). Carefully fold the paper along the y-axis ($x = 0$) and with a sharp point mark the **images** of A and B onto the other side of the y-axis. Label these points A′ and B′ respectively. Join ABB′A′ as shown here.

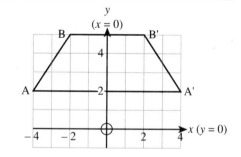

1 Name the shape ABB′A′ and explain the significance of the line $x = 0$.

2 Comment on:
   a The lengths of AB and A′B′.
   b The angle between AA′ and the fold (called the 'mirror line').
   c The distance between B and the fold, and B′ and the fold.

In this Activity you have reflected the line AB in the y-axis ($x = 0$) by folding along the axis. The line A′B′ is called the image of AB. The **resultant** shape is an isosceles trapezium. Can you see the connection between reflection and your previous work on symmetry (Chapter 4)?

REMEMBER
- Reflection is defined by the mirror line.
- To find the mirror line, use the folding method.

Exercise 55

Assume that when a question refers to the x and y axes, the scale used is the same on both axes.

1   Draw any triangle ABC and reflect it in a fold (mirror line) which:
   a Passes through the point A and is labelled m_1.
   b Does not intersect with the triangle and is labelled m_2.
   c Does intersect with the triangle and is labelled m_3, as shown in the diagram. (Leave enough space at the sides to draw the images.)

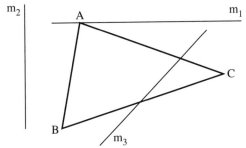

2   The diagram shows six reflections of the shaded triangle. Write down the equation of each line of reflection.

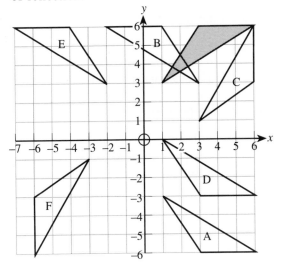

3 Copy the figure below but label the x-axis from 0 to 26. Include flag J: (24, 0), (24, 2), (24, 4) and (22, 3); and also flag K: (24, 0), (24, 2), (24, 4) and (26, 3).

The table below shows details of twelve reflections. Copy this table and complete it by using the details on your diagram.

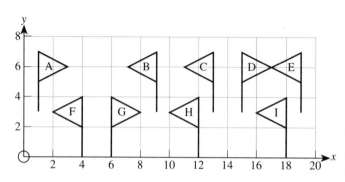

	Object	Reflection in line	Image
a	A	$x = 5$	B
b	F	$x = 5$	
c	G		F
d	A	$x = 7$	
e	D		B
f		$x = 9$	H
g	K		J
h		$x = 12$	G
i		$x = 18$	
j		$x = 10$	A
k	J		G
l		$x = 17$	

What would be the co-ordinates of the image of flag C under a reflection in the line
(i) $x = 101$ (ii) $x = a$?

4 Draw the x and y axes from 5 to -5. Plot the points (0, 5), (4, 4), (0, 0) and join them to form a triangle. Label this triangle 'A'.
  a Reflect $\triangle$A in (i) $x = 0$, and label the image B; (ii) $y = x$, and label the image C.
  b Reflect $\triangle$C in $x = 0$, and label the image D.
  c $\triangle$D can be mapped onto $\triangle$B by a reflection in a certain line. Draw this line on your graph. Write down the equation of this line.

5 Draw the x and y axes from 4 to -4. Draw the lines $y = x$ and $y = -x$ and plot the point Z (3, 2). Reflect Z in **a** $x = 0$ **b** $y = 0$ **c** $y = x$ **d** $y = -x$, and label the images A, B, C and D respectively.
Write down the image of (22, 6) under each of the given reflections.

6 Draw any line XY and mark a point P not on this line. With a pair of compasses, draw several circles of a different radius, with centres on the line XY, to pass through P. Explain how this could be used to construct the image of a point in a given line under reflection.

7 Draw a circle of any radius and mark on its circumference three points X, Y and Z, which are not equal distances (equidistant) apart. Join these points to make a triangle.
Mark on the circumference any point Q. Reflect the point Q in each side of the triangle. Comment on your images.
Repeat this with another circle of a different radius and compare the position of the images with those from the first circle.

MASTERMINDERS

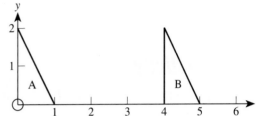

8 Two houses A and B are being built near to the mains drain as shown in the diagram.

The builder wishes to connect both houses to one point using the **minimum** length of pipe. Copy the diagram and devise a method, other than guessing, to find where the connection should be made.

9 Triangle A is reflected in a certain line p and the resulting image is reflected in another line q, so that the final image is triangle B.
Copy the diagram carefully, and draw and label your choices for the lines p and q. Comment on your answers.

___ *Activity 27*

The diagram shows the shaded region (the object) reflected in the line $y = -1$. The **resultant** shape (object plus image) is a rectangle.

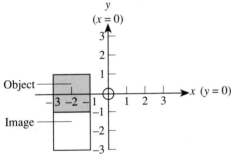

1 Draw four separate sets of x and y axes, each from 3 to -3. For each part **a** to **d**, plot the co-ordinates shown. Join them up with straight lines and shade the enclosed region (the object).
 a $(0, 2), (1, 1), (-2, 0), (-1, -1)$
 b $(1, 0), (3, 0), (-2, -3)$
 c $(2, -2), (0, -2), (-3, 3)$
 d $(0, 3), (-2, 0), (0, -3)$

2 Each object is reflected in a line, and the object and image **together** result in a quadrilateral. Copy and complete this table.

	Reflection in line	Resultant shape
a		Square
b	$y = 0$	
c		Kite
d	$x = 0$	

155

___ **10.3** Rotations

To rotate a shape about a point through a given angle, we use a 'template', as described in the following Activity.

___ *Activity 28*

The problem is to rotate triangle XYZ about the point A through 90° clockwise.

1 Copy the triangle XYZ and mark the point A. (This does not have to be done accurately.)

2 Place a piece of tracing paper over the triangle and the point A. Copy the triangle onto the tracing paper, which we call the template.

3 Put your compass point through the template into the point A. Rotate the template about A through 90° clockwise. Mark through the new position of the triangle. Remove the template and draw the triangle.

These stages are shown here.

In this illustration, at what angle is the line XY to X'Y'?

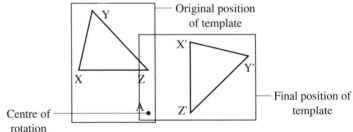

REMEMBER

- Rotation is defined by the angle, direction, and centre of rotation.
- Use the 'template' method to rotate a shape.

___ **Exercise 56**

Assume that when a question refers to the x and y axes, the scale used is the same on both axes.

1 Draw any triangle ABC. Mark a point X inside and a point Y outside. Rotate the triangle
   a about A through 180°   **b** about X through 90° anti-clockwise   **c** about Y through 90° clockwise. Label the images A', B' and C' in each case.

2 The figure alongside shows eight rotations of the shaded triangle. Write down the angle, the direction and the centre of rotation in each case.

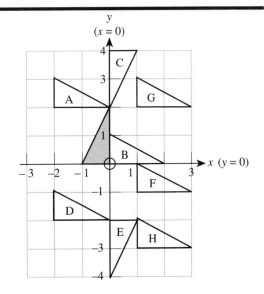

3 Draw any triangle on a template. Put a pin or compass point through any point on the template and rotate through 360°, but change the centre of rotation twice before the whole rotation is complete. What do you notice?

4 The diagram shows an 'up-and-over' door XY, which is 2 m high. It is hinged at A, where A is 50 cm from the door and 1 m from the ground. Find the maximum height of a vehicle which could pass through the door when fully opened.
Investigate what difference it would make if the hinge was in a different place.

5 Draw the x and y axes from 4 to -4. Plot the point A (3, 2). Rotate A about (0, 0) through:
a 90° clockwise   **b** 90° anti-clockwise   **c** 180°.
Write down the co-ordinate of the image in each case. Use your answers to work out the co-ordinate of the image of (16, 61) rotated through the same angles.

MASTERMINDERS

6 A triangle ABC is placed with A at (0, 1), B at (3, 1) and C at (3, 0).
a The triangle is given a 90° clockwise rotation about (3, 0). Find the co-ordinates of the new positions of A, B and C.
b The triangle from its new position is then given a 90° rotation clockwise about some point Q. The overall effect of the two rotations is that the triangle has been given a 180° rotation, from the original position, about (3, 1). What are the final positions of A, B and C?
c Where was Q?

7 The diagram shows a flag in nine different positions. Each flag can be rotated onto one or more of the other flags. For example, flag A can be rotated onto flag F through 90° clockwise about $(-1, 0)$.

The table alongside shows details of thirteen rotations. Copy this table and complete it by using the details on the diagram.

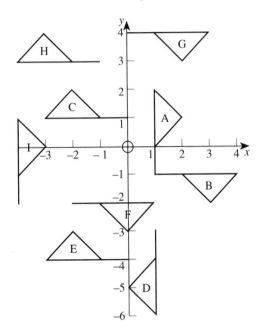

| Object | Rotation | | Image |
	Centre	Angle	
B	$(0, -2)$	90° clockwise	
A	$(1, -2)$	180°	
D			B
G	$(1, -1)$	90° anti-clockwise	
F			I
I	$(-3, -3)$		
	$(0, 2\frac{1}{2})$		G
D	$(-1, -4)$		
	$(3, 1)$		D
	$(-3, 0)$	90° anti-clockwise	
	$(-1\frac{1}{2}, -2\frac{1}{2})$		D
	$(-\frac{1}{2}, 3\frac{1}{2})$		
C		90° anti-clockwise	

___ *Activity 29*

The diagram shows the shaded region (the object) rotated through 180° about $(0, 0)$. The **resultant** shape (object and image together) is a square.

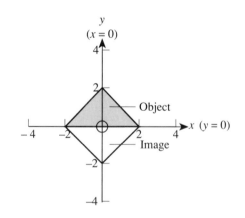

1 Draw five sets of x and y axes, each from 3 to -3. For each part, plot the co-ordinates as shown. Join them up with straight lines and shade the enclosed region (this is the object).

a $(0, 2)$, $(0, -1)$, $(-3, -1)$, $(-1, 2)$
b $(-1, 1)$, $(1, -1)$, $(-1, -3)$, $(-3, -1)$
c $(0, 3)$, $(2, 0)$, $(0, -3)$
d $(0, 1)$, $(1, 3)$, $(1, -2)$
e $(2, 1)$, $(1, 2)$, $(-2, -1)$, $(-1, -2)$

2 Each object is rotated, and the object and image together result in a quadrilateral. Copy and complete this table.

| | Rotation | | Resultant shape |
	Centre	Angle	
a	$(0, \frac{1}{2})$	180°	
b	$(1, -1)$		Rectangle
c	$(0, 0)$		
d			Parallelogram
e		180°	

10.4 Translations

A 'translation' is a movement **without turning**.
In the diagram you will see that triangle A has
been moved to a new position marked triangle B.
We measure this movement by the number of
units it has been moved relative to the x-axis and
by the number of units it has been moved relative
to the y-axis. The movement is therefore:

3 units in a positive direction parallel to the x-axis
1 unit in a positive direction parallel to the y-axis

We write this as a **column vector**, like this: $\begin{pmatrix} 3 \\ 1 \end{pmatrix}$

Why is the translation which takes triangle D to

triangle E given by the column vector $\begin{pmatrix} 3 \\ -2 \end{pmatrix}$?

What is the column vector which describes the
translation to take triangle E back to triangle D?

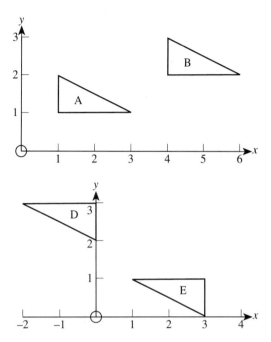

REMEMBER

Translation is defined by a column vector $\begin{pmatrix} x \\ y \end{pmatrix}$ on x and y axes.

Exercise 57

1 Write the column vector which describes the translation of each triangle R to its image S.

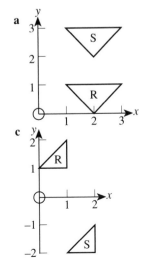

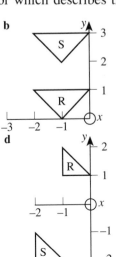

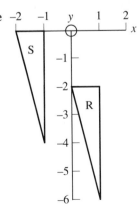

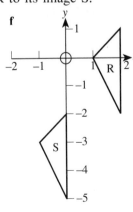

159

2 Draw the x and y axes from 6 to -6. Plot the points $(1, 0)$, $(0, 2)$ and $(-1, 0)$. Join these points to make a triangle and label the triangle T. On your axes plot the image of triangle T under each of the following translations:

$\begin{pmatrix} 5 \\ 0 \end{pmatrix}$ and label the image A

$\begin{pmatrix} 1 \\ -5 \end{pmatrix}$ and label the image B

$\begin{pmatrix} 4 \\ 4 \end{pmatrix}$ and label the image C

$\begin{pmatrix} -5 \\ 3 \end{pmatrix}$ and label the image D

$\begin{pmatrix} 0 \\ -6 \end{pmatrix}$ and label the image E

$\begin{pmatrix} -4 \\ -2 \end{pmatrix}$ and label the image F

3 The diagram shows eight separate translations of the shaded triangle. Write down the column vector to describe each translation.

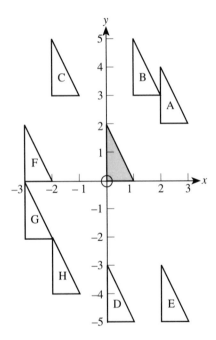

MASTERMINDERS

4 In a certain translation, the image of $(-2, -4)$ is $(2, 4)$. Under the same translation, what is the image of **a** $(-4, -2)$ **b** $(-2, -4)$?

5 In a certain translation the image of $(2, 6)$ is $(-4, -3)$. Under this translation,
a What is the image of $(1234, -4321)$?
b What point has $(0.5, -0.5)$ as its image?

__ 10.5 Miscellaneous transformations

■*EXAMPLE 1*

a Plot the points (5, 2), (5, 4), (2, 4). Join them to form a triangle. Label the triangle T.
b Reflect T in the line $y = 1$ to form triangle R. Draw and label triangle R.
c Rotate T through 90° anti-clockwise about the point $(0, -1)$ to form triangle S. Draw and label triangle S.
d Rotate S through 90° clockwise about $(-5, 1)$ to form triangle U. Draw and label triangle U.
e Describe fully the transformation that maps triangle T onto triangle U.

The answers to parts **a**, **b**, **c** and **d** are shown on this diagram.

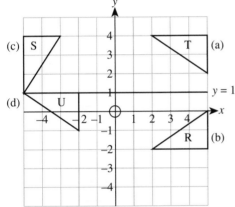

e T is mapped onto U by a translation $\begin{pmatrix} -7 \\ -3 \end{pmatrix}$.

REMEMBER

1 It is **essential** that you plot the first triangle (or other figure) correctly.

2 You should understand the difference between:

- The co-ordinates, say, (5, 2) and (2, 5).
- Reflections in, say, $x = 1$ and $y = 1$.
- Clockwise and anti-clockwise rotations.
- Translations of, say, $\begin{pmatrix} -7 \\ -5 \end{pmatrix}$ and $\begin{pmatrix} 7 \\ 5 \end{pmatrix}$.

___ Exercise 58

For Questions 1, 2 and 3, draw the x and y axes from 5 to -5. Use the same scale for both axes.

1 **a** Plot the points (4, 2), (4, 5), (2, 5). Join them to form a triangle. Label the triangle T.
  b Reflect T in $x = 1$ to form triangle P. Draw and label triangle P.
  c Rotate T through 90° anti-clockwise about (5, 0) to form triangle Q. Draw and label triangle Q.
  d Rotate Q through 90° clockwise about (0, -1) to form triangle R. Draw and label triangle R.
  e Describe fully the transformation that maps R onto T.

2 **a** Plot the points (5, 1), (5, 2), (2, 1). Join them to form a triangle. Label the triangle T.
  b Reflect T in $y = -1$ to form triangle R. Draw and label triangle R.
  c Translate T by $\begin{pmatrix} -2 \\ 2 \end{pmatrix}$ to form triangle U. Draw and label triangle U.
  d Reflect R in $x = 1$ to form triangle S. Draw and label triangle S.
  e Describe fully the transformation that maps S onto U.

3 **a** Plot the points (1, 2), (1, 4), (2, 4). Join them to form triangle P.
  b Draw the image of P under a translation $\begin{pmatrix} -5 \\ -4 \end{pmatrix}$. Label this triangle Q.
  c Reflect P in $y = x$. Label the image R.
  d Rotate R 90° clockwise about (1, 1). Label the image S.
  e Describe fully the transformation that maps S onto P.

4 Describe fully the transformation which maps:
  a R onto Q   **b** P onto T
  c Q onto P   **d** S onto T
  e R onto S   **f** T onto Q

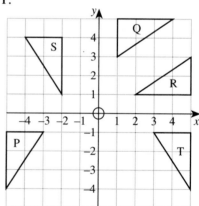

5 Describe fully the transformation which maps:
  a A onto E   **b** C onto B
  c D onto C   **d** B onto A
  e E onto D   **f** B onto D

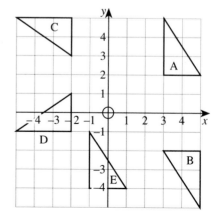

Revision Exercise 10A

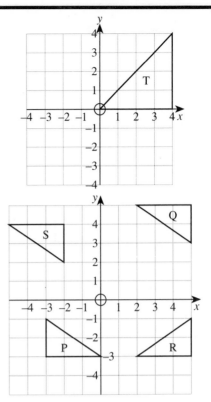

1 Copy the diagram on the right.
  a Write down the equation of the line which is represented by each side of triangle T.
  b Reflect T in $x = 0$ to form triangle R. Draw and label triangle R.
  c Rotate T 90° clockwise about $(0, -1)$. Label the image S.
  d Translate triangle T by $\begin{pmatrix} -5 \\ -5 \end{pmatrix}$ to form triangle U. Draw and label triangle U.

2 Describe as fully as possible the single transformation which maps:
  a Q onto R
  b S onto Q
  c P onto R
  d Q onto P
  e Q onto S
  f P onto S.

Revision Exercise 10B

1 Copy the diagram on the right.
  Apply each of the transformations, given in the table below, to triangle T. Label each image as shown.

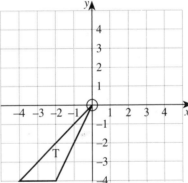

Transformation to triangle T	Label image
Rotation 90° anti-clockwise about $(0, 0)$	A
Reflection in $y = -x$	B
Reflection in $x = 0$	C
Rotation 180° about $(0, 0)$	D
Reflection in $y = x$	E
Rotation 90° clockwise about $(0, 0)$	F
Reflection in $y = 0$	G

2 Describe as fully as possible the single transformation which maps:
  a N onto S
  b M onto T
  c T onto P
  d S onto T
  e P onto Q
  f S onto Q
  g N onto M
  h N onto T
  i M onto P.

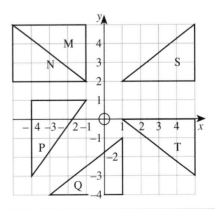

___ Aural Test 2

Twenty questions will be read out to you. You may do any workings on a piece of paper. You will need the following information to answer Questions 11 to 20.

11

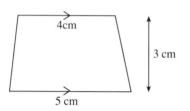

12 Given $14 \times 19 = 266$.

13

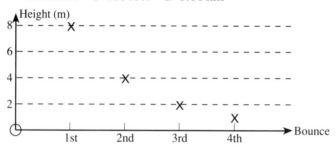

14 and **15** Regular pentagon

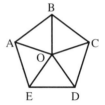

16 a 1000 m   **b** 1000 feet   **c** 100 feet   **d** 0.01 km

17 to 20

___ Puzzlers

1   What number added to six gives the same result as four times the same number?

2   From a piece of paper, cut out a strip about 20 cm long and 3 cm wide. Devise a method to make your strip into a regular pentagon. (No measuring or construction is allowed.)

3   In the addition sum, each of the ten letters represents one of the numbers from zero to nine. Given that K stands for the number three, find the number represented by each of the other nine letters.

```
            A
     M  E  R  R  Y
        X  M  A  S
     _____
     T  U  R  K  E  Y
```

4   In a London Underground station a boy runs up and down two moving staircases, called 'up' and 'down', and the middle (ordinary) staircase called 'middle'.
    a He finds that running down the middle and up the up takes 35 seconds, down the down and up the middle takes 42 seconds and that down the middle and up the middle takes 45 seconds. What is the shortest time he can take to go down and up?
    b He also finds that running down the up and up the up takes 50 seconds, while down the down and up the down takes 72 seconds. How long would it take to go down the up and up the down?

Coursework: The snooker-ball problem

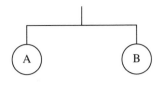

You are given three snooker balls A, B and C, which look identical, and you are told that one is either too heavy or too light.

The problem is to find out which is the odd one and whether it is too heavy or too light. You are allowed only to use an old fashioned beam balance and only to make **two** weighings in part 1.

Figure 1

1 a First weighing (Ball A with Ball B)

There are three possible outcomes. One is shown in Figure 1. The table below shows all three outcomes, together with the conclusions to the results shown in Figure 1. Copy and complete this table.

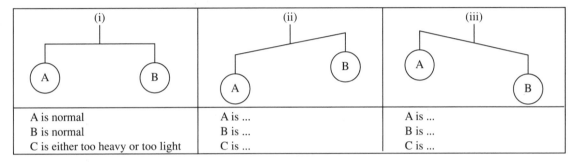

(i)	(ii)	(iii)
A is normal B is normal C is either too heavy or too light	A is ... B is ... C is ...	A is ... B is ... C is ...

b Second weighing (Ball B with Ball C)

Our conclusion from the second weighing depends on the result of the first weighing. If the first weighing produced a balance, with Balls A and B as shown in (i), the conclusions from the second weighing are shown on the table below. Copy and complete this table.

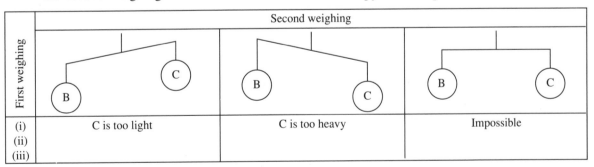

First weighing	Second weighing		
(i) (ii) (iii)	C is too light	C is too heavy	Impossible

EXTENSION

2 You are given four identical balls, A, B, C and D, which look identical, and you are told that one is either too heavy or too light. Find the odd one and whether it is too heavy or too light, with only **three** weighings. List your conclusions on suitable tables. (Your first weighing should be A and B with C and D.)

11 ALGEBRA III

11.1 Basic principles

We use equations to solve a variety of problems.

> **REMEMBER**
>
> 1 Write down the **facts**, if necessary on a diagram.   [F]
> 2 Write down the correct **equation**.   [E]
> 3 **Substitute** the facts into the equation.   [S]
> 4 Show all the **working**.   [W]

■ *EXAMPLE 1*

Richard Noble in 'Thrust 2' set a world land-speed record of 1020 km/h. Find how long it took him to travel 100 m. (*Note*: if the speed v is in km/h, the distance d must be in km.)

[F] $v = 1020$ km/h, $d = 100$ m $= 0.1$ km, time to travel 100 m $= t$.

[E]   **Mean speed** $(v) = \dfrac{\text{Total distance}}{\text{Total time}}$

[S] $1020 = \dfrac{0.1}{t}$

[W] $t = \dfrac{0.1}{1020}$ hours

      $t = \dfrac{0.1}{1020} \times 60 \times 60$ s

      $t = 0.35$ s to 2 SF

■ *EXAMPLE 2*

A triangle has an area of 3.8 cm^2 and a height of 1.9 cm. Find its base (y).

[F]

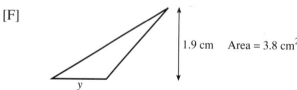

1.9 cm   Area $= 3.8$ cm^2

y

[E]   **Area of triangle** $= \frac{1}{2} \times$ Base $\times$ Height

[S] $3.8 = \frac{1}{2} \times y \times 1.9$

[W] $3.8 = 0.95y$

      $3.8 \div 0.95 = y$

      $y = 4$ cm

166

■ *EXAMPLE 3*

Find the width of a rectangular room of area $14.62\,m^2$ and of length $4.3\,m$.

   [F]   Area $A = 14.62\,m^2$, length $l = 4.3\,m$, width (or breadth) $= w$.

   [E]   **Area of rectangle** $=$ Length $\times$ Breadth

   [S] $14.62 = 4.3 \times w$

   [W] $14.62 \div 4.3 = w$

                        $w = 3.4\,m$

■ *EXAMPLE 4*

One of the largest buildings in the world is the Vehicle Assembly Building at the Kennedy Space Centre, Florida. It has a volume (V) of $5\,511\,040\,m^3$, a length (l) of $218\,m$ and a width (w) of $158\,m$. Find its height.

   [F] $V = 5\,511\,040\,m^3$, $l = 218\,m$, $w = 158\,m$,
           height $= h$

   [E]   **Volume of cuboid** $=$ Length $\times$ Width $\times$ Height

   [S] $5\,511\,040 = 218 \times 158 \times h$

   [W] $\dfrac{5\,511\,040}{218 \times 158} = h$

                   $h = 160\,m$

Exercise 59

1 The diagram shows a carton of orange juice.
    a If its volume is 1 litre, find its height.
      (1 litre $= 1000\,cm^3$).
    b Work out its total surface area.

2 Use the following facts for this question:

Shape	Dimensions in cm (Length $\times$ Breadth)
Rectangle A	49×25
Rectangle B	$x \times 9.8$
Square A	$y \times y$
Rectangle C	$z \times 61$
Square B	$t \times t$

  a Find the area of rectangle A.
  b Find the value of x if rectangle B has the same area as rectangle A.
  c Find the value of y if square A has the same area as rectangle A.
  d Find the perimeter of rectangle A.
  e Find the value of z if rectangle C has the same perimeter as rectangle A.
  f Find the value of t if square B has the same perimeter as rectangle A.

3 Triangles A to D are drawn below, **not to scale**.

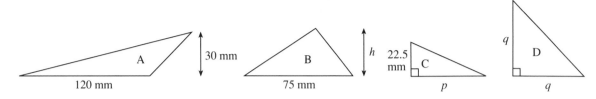

a Find the area of triangle A.
b Find the vertical height (h mm) of triangle B if it has the same area as triangle A.
c Find the value of p if triangle C has the same area as triangle A.
d Find the value of q if triangle D has the same area as triangle A.

4 A world aircraft-speed record is 4680 km/h.
a Work out the distance the aircraft travelled in 15 minutes.
b How long did it take to travel 13 km?

5 ▦ The largest industrial building in the world, by floor area, is a Russian railway factory. If its total volume is 6.075 million cubic metres, its length is 900 m and its average height is 7.5 m, find its width.

MASTERMINDERS

6 ▦ The main runway at Gatwick is 3.15 km long and 100 m wide.
a Find its area in hectares. (1 hectare = 10 000 m^2)
b If 1.5 cm of snow falls over the area, estimate the mass of snow on the runway. (Take the density of snow as 0.2 g/cm^3.)

7 ▦ The greatest number of people ever to get into a telephone kiosk, at the same time, is 32. The internal dimensions of the kiosk were 80 cm by 80 cm by 2.4 m.
When this record was established, 15% of the volume was **not** taken up with bodies. Work out the mean volume of each of the 32 people, to the nearest tenth of a cubic metre.

8 ▦ The volume of material blown out by the most recent volcano on Mount St Helen's was estimated to be 2.7 km^3, which is thirty times the volume of all New York's skyscrapers. If there are 3000 skyscrapers in New York, what is the average volume of a skyscraper in m^3?

11.2 Area

Activity 30

1 We can work out the area of a parallelogram and a trapezium by drawing a diagonal.

a [F]   See diagram
[E]   Total area = Area I + Area II
[S]   Area = ($\frac{1}{2}$ × 6 × 4) + ($\frac{1}{2}$ × 6 × 4)
[W]   Area = 12 + 12 = 24 cm^2

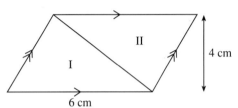

b Show that the area of this trapezium is 20 cm^2.

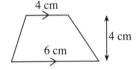

2 Show that the area of the two figures is given by the equations below.

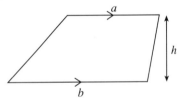

Area of parallelogram = Base × Height = ah **Area of trapezium** = $\frac{h}{2}(a + b)$

To work out the area of a more complicated figure, it may be necessary to divide it up. Look carefully at the following example.

■ EXAMPLE 1

Find the area of this shape.

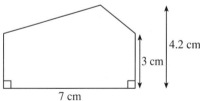

(First draw the figure and then divide it up into a rectangle and a triangle. Label each region and include all the dimensions.)

[F]   See diagram
[E]   Total area = Area T + Area R
[S]   Total area = ($\frac{1}{2}$ × 7 × 1.2) + (7 × 3)
[W]   = (3.5 × 1.2) + (21)
            = 25.2 cm^2

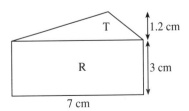

169

___ Exercise 60

For each question find the area of the given figure. (A broken line indicates an axis of symmetry.)

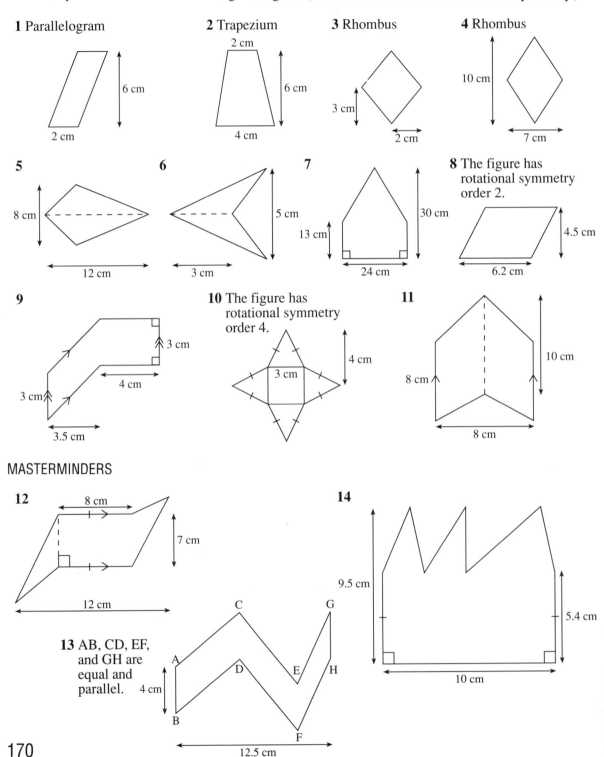

1 Parallelogram

6 cm

2 cm

2 Trapezium

2 cm

6 cm

4 cm

3 Rhombus

3 cm

2 cm

4 Rhombus

10 cm

7 cm

5

8 cm

12 cm

6

5 cm

3 cm

7

30 cm

13 cm

24 cm

8 The figure has rotational symmetry order 2.

4.5 cm

6.2 cm

9

3 cm

4 cm

3 cm

3.5 cm

10 The figure has rotational symmetry order 4.

4 cm

3 cm

11

8 cm

10 cm

8 cm

MASTERMINDERS

12

8 cm

7 cm

12 cm

13 AB, CD, EF, and GH are equal and parallel.

4 cm

A

C

D

E

G

H

B

F

12.5 cm

14

9.5 cm

5.4 cm

10 cm

— More calculations using area

— Exercise 61

Questions 1 to 7 ask for the calculation of a length in a given figure whose area is given. Remember to show your working clearly. Find the value of x in Questions 1 to 4.

1   **2** A rhombus   **3** An arrow-head   **4**

Area = 28 cm²   4 cm   3 cm   Area = 18 cm²   Area = 35 cm²   7 cm   Area = 35 cm² x 10 cm x

5   The area of the trapezium is $20\,\text{cm}^2$. Copy and complete the table.

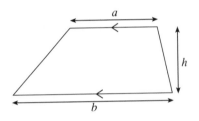

	\textit{Length (cm)}		
	a	b	h
a	10	70	
b	2.8	2.2	
c		3	12.5
d	4		5
e		2.7	10
f	3.8		6.25

MASTERMINDERS

6   This figure has rotational symmetry order 4. If the total area is $48\,\text{cm}^2$, find the value of x.

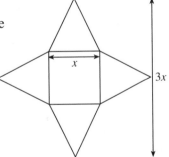

x $3x$

7   A square has an area of $50\,\text{cm}^2$. Find the length of its diagonal.

8   In this rectangle, LM is parallel to ON. Find the ratio of the total shaded region to the whole rectangle.

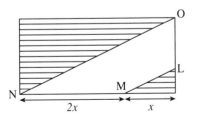

O   L   N   M $2x$ x

___ 11.3 Graphs and area

To work out the area of some figures it may be necessary to 'box up' the given figure. Look at the following example.

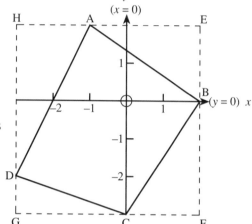

■ *EXAMPLE 1*

Find the area of a quadrilateral ABCD, with vertices A (−1, 2), B (2, 0), C (0, −3), D (−3, −2). Give your answer in square units.

    [F]   See diagram

    [E]   Area ABCD = Area EFGH − Area of 4△s

    [S]   Area = $25 - 3 - 3 - 1\frac{1}{2} - 4$

    [W]   Area = 13.5 square units

___ Exercise 62

Assume that when a question refers to x and y axes, the scale is the same on both.

1   Plot the given points on suitable axes. Join up to make two triangles. Work out the area of each in square units.

    a (−5, −1), (−4, −1), (−1, 7)

    b (−3, 1), (−1, 1), (0, 4)

2   **a** Write down the co-ordinates of the points A, B, C and D.

    b Name the type of triangle: (i) ABD   (ii) ABC (iii) AOB.

    c Name the quadrilateral ABCD.

    d Write down the equations of the lines AC and BD, and the x and y axes.

    e Write down the equations of the two axes of symmetry.

    f How could you use the figure to show that AB is parallel to DC?

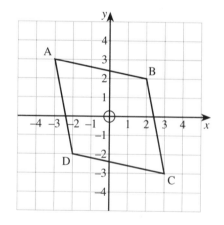

3   Write down the equation of the line joining the following pairs of points:

    a (7, 9), (7, −14)   **b** (3, 9), (14, 9)

    c (5, 5), (−3, −3)   **d** (−6, 6), (0, 0)

    e (−29, 5), (−29, 55)   **f** (−67, 67), (67, −67)

    g (−67, 67), (−67, −67) **h** (67, 67), (−67, −67)

4 ABCD is a quadrilateral whose vertices have the following co-ordinates:
A (3, 2), B (4, −3), C (−4, −5), D (−2, 4).
a On suitable axes, plot the points A, B, C and D. Join them up to form a quadrilateral.
b Find the area of ABCD in square units.

5 **a** Name each of the seven quadrilaterals and write down the equation of any axes of symmetry.
b Work out the area of each quadrilateral in square units.

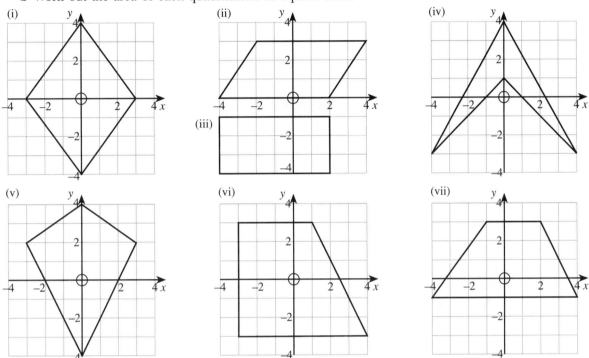

(i)   (ii)   (iv)   (iii)   (v)   (vi)   (vii)

For Questions 6 to 16, plot the co-ordinates given on separate axes each from 5 to −7. Use the information given in the table below to complete each figure. Copy and complete the table. Remember to use the same scale on both axes. (Each co-ordinate is a vertex of the figure.)

	Co-ordinates given	Name of figure	Remaining co-ordinates	Axis of symmetry (if any)	Area of figure
6	(−3, 2), (3, 0), (3, 4)		None		
7	(4, 4), (−2, 5)			$y = x$	
8	(−4, −4), (4, 4)	Right-angled isosceles		$y = -x$	
9	(−5, −1), (−1, 3), (3, −1)		None		
10	(−1, 4), (4, −1), (1, −4)	Rectangle			
11	(−2, 4), (3, −3), (−2, −1), (3, 1)		None		
12	(0, 3), (5, 5), (0, 0)			$y = x$	
13	(1, 3), (−1, −1), (−4, −1)			$y = -1$	
14	(−3, 0), (0, 3), (5, 2)	Right-angled trapezium			
15	(−3, 0), (−1, −3), (−5, −3)	Parallelogram			
16	(2, 4), (0, −1)			$y = -1, x = 2$	

17 Draw three x and y axes, the y-axis from 4 to -4 and the the x-axis from 8 to -8. Use a separate set of axes for each part and plot the co-ordinates given. Calculate the area of the resultant figure in square units. Show your working clearly.

a (7, 4), (3,-3), (-6, 1)
b (7, 1), (-4, 4), (-6, 2), (-3, -3)
c (4, 4), (3, 0), (4, -4), (0, -3), (-4, -4), (-3, 0), (-4, 4), (0, 3)

MASTERMINDERS

18 The points (0, 0) and (-3, -3) are two vertices of a square. Write down all the possible pairs of co-ordinates to complete the square.

19 The points (a, 0), (0, a) and (0, $-a$) are three vertices of a square.
a Write down the fourth vertex.
b Work out the area of the square in terms of a, giving your answer in square units.

20 The points (a, b), (a, $-b$) and (0, c) are the three vertices of a triangle. Find its area in terms of a and b, giving your answer in square units.

21 A figure drawn on x and y axes has the following axes of symmetry: $x = 0$, $y = 0$, $y = x$ and $y = -x$. Two vertices are (3, 3) and (0, 4). Find the others.

22 ABCD is a quadrilateral whose vertices have the following co-ordinates: A(-4, 0), B(0, 4), C(4, 0), D(0, -6). The point D is moved in a straight line towards B. **Investigate** what happens to the shape of the quadrilateral at each co-ordinate.

— 11.4 Speed

Some speed questions involve two or more different speeds. For such questions, always write down the facts on a line which represents the distance of the journey. Look carefully at the following example.

■ EXAMPLE 1

Clare leaves home on her bicycle and aims to arrive at Andrew's house at a certain time. If she rides at 15 mph, she will arrive an hour early but if she rides at 10 mph she will arrive an hour late. Find the distance she cycles.

Let the time she intends to cycle $= t$ hours.
Let the journey distance $= d$ miles.

$$\textit{Journey 1} \quad v = 15 \text{ mph}, \, t = (t - 1)\,\text{h}$$

Clare's house ●————————————————————● Andrew's house

$$\textit{Journey 2} \quad v = 10 \text{ mph}, \, t = (t + 1)\,\text{h}$$

Journey 1: $15 = \dfrac{d}{t - 1}$

                $15(t - 1) = d$ [i]

Journey 2: $10 = \dfrac{d}{t + 1}$

                $10(t + 1) = d$ [ii]

Equation [i] = Equation [ii]

Therefore $15(t - 1) = 10(t + 1)$

                $15t - 15 = 10t + 10$

                $5t = 25$

                $t = 5$

Substituting $t = 5$ into Equation [i] gives journey distance $d = 60$ miles.

___ Exercise 63

1   Travelling at 36 mph I can drive from my house to my work in 20 minutes. If I wish to reduce my travelling time to 15 minutes, by how much must I increase my speed?

2   Driving home through the rush hour one evening, I covered the first two miles at a mean speed of 6 mph and the next ten miles at a mean speed of 20 mph. What was my mean speed for the whole journey?

3   A car does 15 miles at 30 mph, then 10 miles at 60 mph. What is its mean speed for the the whole journey?

4   Alan can run the 100 metres in 16 seconds and Harry can run it in 14 seconds. If they have a race, by what distance does Harry beat Alan?

5   Christine runs at 5 m/s and is given a start of 15 m by Alexandra who runs at 7 m/s. How far has Christine run when Alexandra overtakes her?

6   A train does a journey in five hours. Find the percentage increase in its mean speed needed to do the journey in four hours.

7   A journey of 210 miles by car took six hours. How long will it take if the car's mean speed is increased by 5 mph?

MASTERMINDERS

8   A man walks x miles at 4 mph. He then travels by bus for $6x$ miles at 16 mph. Write down the time he takes for each part of the journey. If the whole journey takes one hour, form an equation and find x.

9   A coach travelling at 80 km/h overtook a lorry travelling, in the same direction, at 70 km/h. If the lorry had a length of 30 m and the coach had a length of 20 m, how long did the coach take to completely overtake the lorry?

___ 11.5 Formulae

A formula is an equation which is used to help solve problems. In this section you will see how formulae can be used in a variety of ways.

___ Activity 31

Doctors and dieticians use the following formula to work out a person's Body Mass Index (BMI). This index is used to determine whether a person is over or under weight. Most 12-year-olds have a BMI between 14 and 20.

$$\text{BMI} = \frac{\text{Mass in kg}}{(\text{Height in m})^2}$$

1   Work out your own BMI and comment on the result.

2   Work out, to 2 SF, the normal range of mass, for a 12-year-old, for each of the following heights: 1.40 m, 1.45 m, 1.50 m, 1.55 m, 1.60 m, 1.65 m.
Represent your answers on a bar chart.

3   Seb Coe, one-time holder of seven world athletics records, had a BMI of 19. If his height is 188 cm, find his mass to the nearest kilogram.

4   Find out the mass and height of other well known sportspeople and work out their BMI.

___ Activity 32

In the Coursework on page 124, you were given a formula (shown below) to find the cost of electricity (C), in pence, if an appliance of P kW is used for T hours, where R is the charge per unit of electricity in pence.

$$C = PTR$$

In this Activity, remember to use the correct units for C, P and T. Take R to be 8p unless stated otherwise.

1   A 3 kW radiator is accidentally left on in a holiday home after the summer holidays. Find the cost to the owner if the radiator was on for 182 days.

2   For how long could you leave on a 2 kW fire for £1 of electricity?

3   For how long could you leave on an 8 kW shower for 1p of electricity?

4 The appliances shown in the table below are each used for seven hours. Work out the cost in each case, if the charge for 'Night units' is 2p per unit and the charge for 'Day units' is 8p per unit. Copy and complete this table.

Appliance	Power (kW)	Cost (£)	
		Night units	Day units
Shower	8		
Radiator	2.4		
Oven	3		
Microwave	0.5		

Represent these figures by drawing two lines on a graph. Use a scale of 2 cm to 1 kW on the horizontal axis and 2 cm to £1 on the vertical axis. Explain why the lines are straight and why they pass through the same point.

Exercise 64

1 A school has an epidemic of mumps. The number of pupils off sick on the nth day of February is N, where

$$N = 10 + 2(n - 3)$$

a How many were off sick on the fifth day of February?
b Find the day on which there were 44 pupils off sick.

2 ABCD and BDFE are squares. Let EF = d. Show that the area of ABCD is given by the following formula:

$$\text{Area ABCD} = \frac{d^2}{2}$$

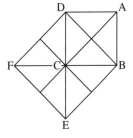

a Find the area of a square of diagonal 3 cm.
b Find the length of a diagonal of a square of area 32 cm^2.

3 People started queuing up outside Wimbledon six hours before the gates opened. They came at a steady rate of 200 every hour. Copy and complete this table.

a If N represents the number of people queuing and t the number of hours before the gates open, write down an equation relating N and t.
b Use your equation to find the number of people queuing 2 h 15 min before the gates open.
c When there are 350 people in the queue, how much longer is it before the gates open?

Number of hours before gates open	Number of people queuing
6	0
5	
4	
3	
2	
1	
0	
t	

4 A missile is fired upwards from the top of a cliff. The height h metres above the cliff t seconds after firing is given by this formula:

$h = 100t - 5t^2$

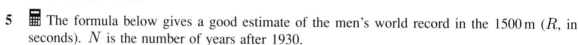

How high, above or below the cliff top, is the missile after the following number of seconds:
a 10 **b** 20 **c** 21?

5 ▦ The formula below gives a good estimate of the men's world record in the 1500 m (R, in seconds). N is the number of years after 1930.

$R = 231 - 0.39N$

a What do you think the world record was in 1930?
b Estimate the world record set by Seb Coe in 1985.
c Estimate when the world record is likely to be 3 minutes 25 seconds.
d The world record in 1975 was 3 minutes 32.2 seconds. Write down the difference, in seconds, between this time and the time given by the formula.

6 ▦ The formula below gives a method to convert a temperature C, in Celsius (°C) to a temperature F, in Fahrenheit (°F).

$$F = \frac{9C + 160}{5}$$

a Use this formula to convert:
  (i) 10 °C to °F (ii) −5 °C to °F (iii) 68 °F to °C (iv) 14 °F to °C
b When is $F = C$?
c (i) Explain why a 'rough-and-ready' method to convert °C to °F is to double C and add 30. Write down this 'rough-and-ready' formula.
  (ii) Use your formula to convert each of the temperatures shown in part **a**. How accurate are your answers?

MASTERMINDERS

7 ▦ Because the Earth is round we can only see to the horizon, d miles away. The distance d, in miles, that the horizon appears to be away, from a height h, in feet, above sea level is given by the formula:

$d = \sqrt{1.5h}$

a What is the distance to the horizon from
  (i) 24 feet (ii) 600 feet above sea level?
b How much further can I see if I go up another 18 feet from 24 feet? Give your answer to the nearest mile.
c How high must I be to see 12 miles to the horizon?
d If you are standing on the beach with your eye six feet above sea level, and can just see the top of the funnel of a liner (96 feet high), how far out to sea is the liner?

8 A rectangular block has a square base of side x cm. The total surface area of the block is A cm². Show that its volume V is given by the equation:

$$V = \frac{x(A - 2x^2)}{4} \text{ cm}^3$$

The block has a volume of $54\,\text{cm}^3$ and a surface area of $90\,\text{cm}^2$. If it is resting on the square base, find its height.

9 A box is in the shape of a cuboid. It has faces of area x cm², y cm², z cm². Write down the volume of the box in terms of x, y and z.

11.6 Inequalities

Look at the diagrams (i), (ii) and (iii) in the Coursework on page 165.

In diagram (i) A equals B   or A = B
In diagram (ii) A is greater than B or A > B
In diagram (iii) A is less than B   or A < B

REMEMBER

> means 'greater than'
≥ means 'greater than or equal to'
< means 'less than'
≤ means 'less than or equal to'

Now look at three similar examples below:

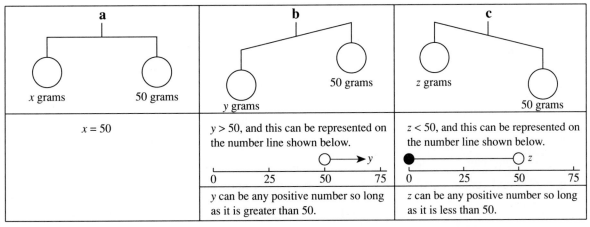

a	b	c
$x = 50$	$y > 50$, and this can be represented on the number line shown below.	$z < 50$, and this can be represented on the number line shown below.
	y can be any positive number so long as it is greater than 50.	z can be any positive number so long as it is less than 50.

(*Note*: neither y nor z can equal 50, so the circle above 50 is left unshaded. However z can equal zero, so the circle above zero **is** shaded in.)

Another example is the number of passengers who can be seated in a bus. Suppose a certain bus has 70 seats. Then if n is the number of passengers on the bus, it must obey the inequality:

$$n \leq 70$$

This number line illustrates this example.

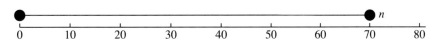

(*Note*: both circles are shaded in because n can equal either zero or 70.)

179

■ *EXAMPLE 1*

Draw a number line to represent each of the following inequalities, given that the letters represent positive numbers only:

a $x > 5$

b $y \geqslant 3$

c $z < 4$ and can equal zero

d $p < 7$ and cannot equal zero

e $q \leqslant 6$ and can equal zero.

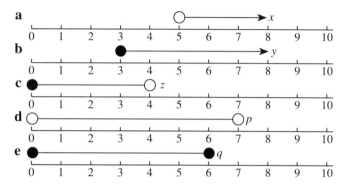

— **Exercise 65**

1   Draw the number line to represent each of the following inequalities: **a** $x > 3$ **b** $y > 5$
   c $z > 3.5$ **d** $t \geqslant 2$ **e** $u \geqslant 6$ **f** $v \geqslant 2.5$

2   Write down the inequality which is represented by each of the following number lines.

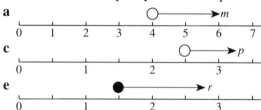

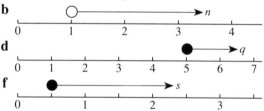

3   Draw a number line to represent each of the following inequalities, given that the letters represent positive numbers only.

   a $x < 4$ and cannot equal zero.

   c $z < 8$ and can equal zero.

   e $n \leqslant 6$ and can equal zero.

   g $q \leqslant 9$ and cannot equal zero.

   b $y < 6\frac{1}{2}$ and cannot equal zero.

   d $m < 3\frac{1}{2}$ and can equal zero.

   f $p \leqslant 1\frac{1}{2}$ and can equal zero.

   h $r \leqslant 4\frac{1}{2}$ and cannot equal zero.

4   Write down the inequality which is represented by each of the following number lines. State whether or not each letter can equal zero.

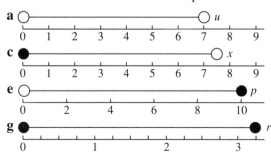

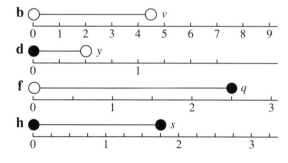

Solving an inequality

Make sure you can solve the equations in Exercise 19 (page 39) before starting this part.

Sometimes we need to solve an inequality to find the range of values which is represented by the letter. We use the same method used for solving equations **except** when we divide or multiply by a negative number. In this case the inequality sign is reversed. (See Example 4.)

■ *EXAMPLE 2*

Solve the inequality $3x - 4 > 8$ and represent the solution on a number line.

$$3x - 4 > 8 \quad \text{(Add 4 to both sides)}$$
$$3x > 12 \quad \text{(Divide both sides by 3)}$$

Therefore $\quad x > 4$

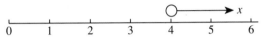

(Note that a number $\leqslant 4$ will not satisfy the original inequality. For example, when $x = 1$, $3x - 4 > 8$ becomes $-1 > 8$.)

■ *EXAMPLE 3*

Solve the inequality $\frac{x}{3} + 2 \leqslant 5$. Given that x stands for positive values only and can equal zero, draw a number line to represent the solution. State the whole number values (called 'integers') which satisfy the inequality.

$$\frac{x}{3} + 2 \leqslant 5 \quad \text{(Subtract 2 from both sides)}$$
$$\frac{x}{3} \leqslant 3 \quad \text{(Multiply both sides by 3)}$$

Therefore $\quad x \leqslant 9$

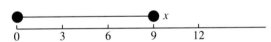

The whole number values of x are 0 to 9 inclusive. (Note that when $x > 9$, $\frac{x}{3} + 2 > 5$.)

■ *EXAMPLE 4*

Solve the inequality $2(4 - x) < x - 4$.

$$2(4 - x) < x - 4 \quad \text{(Expand brackets)}$$
$$8 - 2x < x - 4 \quad \text{(Collect up } x \text{ terms on LHS and numbers on RHS)}$$
$$-2x - x < -4 - 8$$
$$-3x < -12 \quad \text{(Divide both sides by } -3)$$
$$x > \frac{-12}{-3} \quad \textbf{(Inequality sign reversed)}$$

Therefore $\quad x > 4$

(Note that when $x \leqslant 4$, $2(4 - x) \geqslant x - 4$.)

REMEMBER

- Collect up the lettered terms on the lefthand side.
- When dividing or multiplying both sides by a negative number, the inequality sign is reversed.

___ Exercise 66

For Questions 1 to 6, solve the inequality and represent the solution on a number line.

1 $4x - 9 > 11$ **2** $8y - 15 < 41$ **3** $3z + 14 > 32$

4 $5t + 13 \geqslant 28$ **5** $6u + 17 \geqslant 65$ **6** $\frac{v}{2} + 8 \leqslant 13$

For Questions 7 to 14, solve the inequality. Given that the letter represents positive values only and can equal zero, draw a number line to represent the solution. State the integer values which satisfy the inequality.

7 $8x + 9 \leqslant 41$ **8** $5y + 13 \leqslant 48$ **9** $6z - 17 \leqslant 13$

10 $25m - 21 \leqslant 29$ **11** $12n - 49 < 47$ **12** $\frac{p}{2} - 1\frac{1}{2} < 1\frac{1}{2}$

13 $\frac{q}{3} + 1 < 2.5$ **14** $\frac{r}{4} + \frac{3}{4} < 1.2$

For Questions 15 to 30, solve the inequality.

15 $-2x < 14$ **16** $-3x \leqslant 15$ **17** $24 \geqslant 4x$

18 $10 < 3x$ **19** $2 - 3x < 6$ **20** $4 - 2x > -8$

21 $3 + 2x \leqslant 8x$ **22** $7x + 5 \leqslant 13x - 1$ **23** $3(2 - x) \leqslant x - 2$

24 $x + 2 \leqslant 4(x + 3)$ **25** $4(x - 5) > 12x$ **26** $2(x + 2) \geqslant 3\frac{1}{2}x$

MASTERMINDERS

27 $\frac{3x}{2} < 2x + 3$ **28** $4 - 3x < \frac{2x}{3}$ **29** $2 \div x > 3$

30 $3 > \frac{3}{x} + 3$

31 Investigate a method to solve $x^2 > 4$.

___ Revision Exercise 11A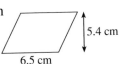

1 Find the area of each of the figures: **a** Parallelogram **b** Trapezium

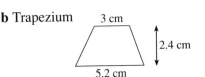

5.4 cm

6.5 cm

3 cm

2.4 cm

5.2 cm

2 Draw the x and y axes from 5 to -5 using the same scale on both axes. Plot the points A (4, 4), B (4, -4) and C (-4, 4). Join up the points to form triangle ABC.
   a Write down the equations of the lines AB, AC, CB.
   b Write down the equation of the axis of symmetry of ABC.
   c Work out the area of triangle ABC.

3 **a** Find the volume of a rectangular box 15 cm long, 10 cm wide and 25 cm deep.
   b A packet of sugar, of volume 750 cm³, is emptied into the box. Work out the depth of sugar in the box.
   c Each packet of sugar weighs 1 kg. How many kilograms of sugar will the box hold when full?

4 The area of a rhombus can be worked out by multiplying together the length of each diagonal and dividing the result by two.
   a If the length of one diagonal is x cm, the length of the other is y cm, and the area is A cm², write down the area (A) in terms of x and y.
   b Find the area of a rhombus which has diagonals of length 12 cm and 15 cm.

5 When the high explosive 'Semtex' is used, it explodes at 8000 km/s. At that rate, how long would it take, in theory, to reach the Moon which is 400 000 km away?

6 Solve the inequality: $2x + 1 < 11$.

___ Revision Exercise 11B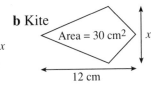

1 Find the value of x in the following: **a** Trapezium **b** Kite

7 cm

Area = 42 cm²

9.8 cm

x

Area = 30 cm²

x

12 cm

2 Draw the x and y axes from 5 to -5, using the same scale on both axes. Plot the points A (-1, 4), B (-4, -2) and C (5, -5). Join up the points to form triangle ABC. Work out the area of triangle ABC in square units.

3 A man drives on a motorway at 60 mph for half an hour and then at 66 mph for 1 hour. What is his mean speed over the $1\frac{1}{2}$ hours?

4 The figure shows an arrowhead of area A cm².
   a Show that the area of the figure is given by the equation: $A = \frac{x}{2}(z - y)$.
   b Find the value of y, when $x = 8$ cm, $z = 7.5$ cm and $A = 17.2$ cm².

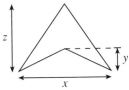

z

x

y

5 Sound travels at 300 m/s. Light travels so fast that it arrives almost instantaneously. If the time between a flash of lightning and its clap of thunder is 4.2 seconds, how far away is the storm?

6 Find the largest whole number (x) which satisfies the equation: $5 - 6x > 4(x - 5)$.

___ Aural Test 3

Twenty questions will be read out to you. You may do any workings on a piece of paper. You will need the following information to answer Questions 11 to 20.

11 and **12**

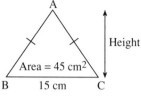

13 and **14**

	Prices
Coke	46p
Kit Kat	28p
Crisps	17p

15 Given 234 ÷ 13 = 18.

16 a 140 kg **b** 70 kg **c** 300 kg

17 to **20**

    a 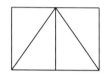   **b**    **c** 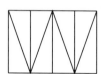   **d**

___ Puzzlers

1 Unfortunately the final table of the local ice-hockey league table got lost on its way to the editor of the local paper. However, the report arrived at her office, and this is what it said:

'Each team played every other team twice, and the final order was alphabetical. Only two teams won more than half their matches, but only one team lost more than half its matches. No two teams won the same number of matches. No team was unbeaten and only Barnwell failed to draw at least one match. Ashton won the same number of matches that Elton lost. Deene lost half their matches and Cotterstock got eight points. No two teams ended up with the same number of points.'

(A win counts as two points and a draw counts as one point.)

This information was enough to enable the editor to draw up the final league table. Are you as clever as she is? If you are, copy and complete the table:

Team	Played	Won	Drew	Lost	Points
1					
2					
3					
4					
5					

2 What is the largest number which will divide into 177, 228 and 262, leaving the same remainder in each case?

Coursework: Active Maths Puzzle

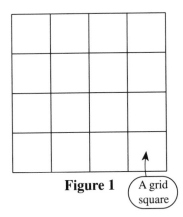

Figure 1 (A grid square)

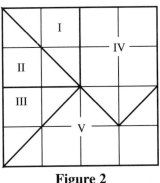

Figure 2

In this Coursework you are going to make the seven-piece Active Maths Puzzle. All your constructions must be done using only your ruler and pencil, but you can use your protractor to draw right angles.

Figure 1 shows a grid of 16 squares. (These must be drawn so that the width of each square is the width of your ruler.)

1 **a** Make a neat accurate drawing of the puzzle shown in Figure 2. Label each piece as shown.
  b With your ruler and pencil, draw four grid squares (in the shape of a square). Use these squares to make the sixth piece of the puzzle. This is a square which has a side length equal to the diagonal of a grid square. Label this VI.
  c Use your two neat drawings, as templates, to mark through onto a piece of card each of the six pieces of the puzzle. Cut out the six pieces from card and label them I, II, III, etc.

2 **a** Find the area of each piece of the puzzle, if the width of your ruler is (i) 2 cm (ii) x cm. Copy the following table and enter your results.

	Grid square width (cm)	Area (cm²)						Total area (cm²)
		I	II	III	IV	V	VI	
(i)	2							
(ii)	x							

  b (i) Using all six card pieces, fit them together to make a square (the six-piece puzzle.) Draw a diagram to show how you have done it.
  (ii) Measure the width of your ruler in cm. (This is the value of x in part 2a.) Use this measurement to work out the total area of your six-piece square and hence find its side length. Compare this value with the side length of your actual six-piece puzzle.

EXTENSION

3 Figure 3 shows the seven-piece puzzle. The dimensions of the seventh piece are shown below.

Figure 3

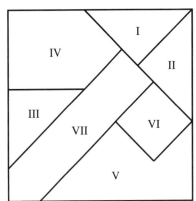

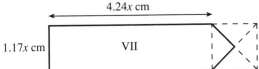

4.24x cm

1.17x cm   VII

  a Find, in terms of x, (i) the area of the seventh piece
  (ii) the side length of the seven-piece puzzle.
  b Make the seventh piece to complete your puzzle.

12 GEOMETRY II

12.1 Basic principles

Triangle construction

REMEMBER

- If a diagram is not given, draw a **quick rough sketch** and include all the facts.
- Use a sharp pencil and do not press too hard.
- Hold your pair of compasses with one hand and leave in all your construction lines.
- Start by drawing a straight line slightly longer than the given length.
- Label the completed figure and write any answers at the side.

Angle of elevation

The diagram shows the **angle of elevation** from a point P to the top of a building.

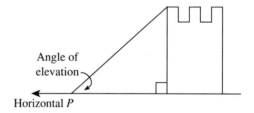

Scale drawing

REMEMBER

- First convert all measurements, using the scale given.
- Use a sharp pencil and do not press too hard.
- Use a protractor to draw any right angles.
- Label your drawing and write down the scale used.

— Exercise 67

1 Construct the following triangles. Measure the perpendicular height of each and hence work out the area of each triangle.

a

60°   55°
8 cm

b

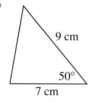

9 cm

50°
7 cm

c

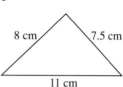

8 cm   7.5 cm

11 cm

2 Construct two triangles ABC, each of a different shape, where BC = 10.5 cm, angle ABC = 40° and AC = 8 cm. Measure the perpendicular height of A above BC in each triangle and hence work out the area of each.

3 On horizontal ground, the distance to the base of a building is 25 m and the angle of elevation to the top is 56°. Make a suitable scale drawing to find the height of the building.

4 The diagram shows the plan of a rectangular garden and garage. Make a scale drawing using a scale of 1 : 200. Use your drawing to find the actual distance AB to the nearest 10 cm.

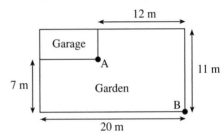

— **12.2** Bearings and maps

Bearings are measured **clockwise from the North**, in degrees. Look carefully at the following examples:

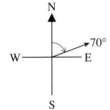

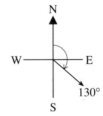

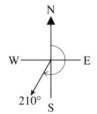

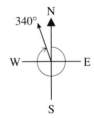

■*EXAMPLE 1*

The bearing of B from A is 300°. What is the bearing of A from B?

First draw the 'North' line through each point.

The bearing of A from B = 180° − 60° = 120°.

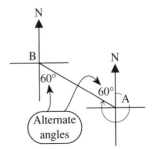

187

REMEMBER

- Bearings are measured clockwise from the North.
- Always draw the 'North' line through each point.
- Look for alternate angles to help find the value of the bearing.

— **Exercise 68**

For Questions 1 to 8, work out **a** the bearing of B from A   **b** the bearing of A from B.
Comment on your answers.

1 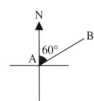   **2** 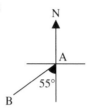   **3** 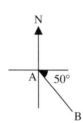   **4**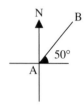

5 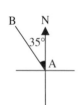   **6** 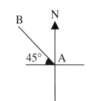   **7** 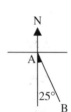   **8**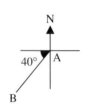

9   Copy and complete the table.

	Bearing of B from A	*Bearing of A from B*
a	200°	
b	025°	
c	125°	
d	320°	

MASTERMINDER

10 The bearing of A from D = 025°, of B from A = 125°, of C from B = 230°,
of D from C = 280°, of C from A = 165°. Find the bearing of B from D.

REMEMBER

On a map-grid, Eastings come before Northings.

___ *Activity 33*

This map-grid is drawn to a scale of 2 cm to 1 km.

1 **Grid reference.** Write down:
   a The four-figure grid reference of the grid square containing point D.
   b The six-figure grid reference of the points A, B, C, D, E, F.

2 **Scale.** Work out:
   a The scale of the map-grid in the form $1 : n$ where n is an integer.
   b The actual distance, in km, represented by AB, AC and BC.

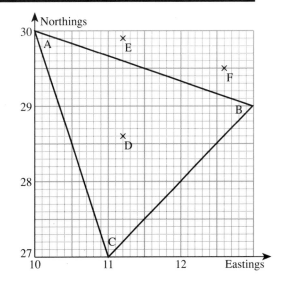

3 **Bearings.** Use your protractor to measure the bearings shown in this table. Copy and complete the table.

		Bearing from		
		A	B	C
	A	0°		
To	B		0°	045°
	C			0°

4 Work out the area of triangle ABC in cm². Work out, in square kilometres, the actual area which this triangle represents.

___ Exercise 69

1 This map-grid shows the positions of two points A and B. It is drawn to a scale of 4 cm to 1 km.
   a Write down the grid reference of the points A and B.
   b Measure the bearing of (i) A from B (ii) B from A.
   c Explain why the scale of the map-grid can be written as 1 : 25 000.
   d Work out the actual distance represented by the line AB.

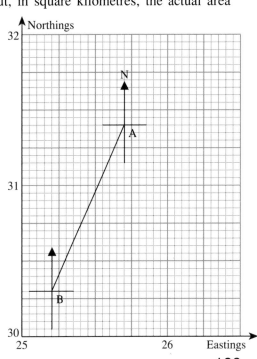

189

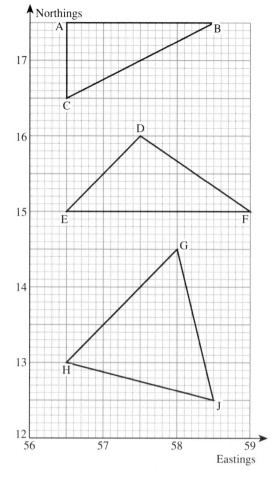

2 This map-grid shows the position of three triangles. It is drawn to a scale of 2 cm to 1 km.

a Explain why the scale of the map-grid can be written 1 : 50 000.

b Work out the area of each of the triangles in cm².

c Work out the actual area which is represented by each of the three triangles.

d Measure the following bearings: (i) D to F (ii) F to D (iii) A to B (iv) E to H (v) J to H (vi) G to H.

e A girl walks round the perimeter of the triangle GHJ. How far does she walk?

3 On graph paper, copy the Eastings and Northings used in Question 2. Plot the points A, which has a grid reference of 585130, B, which has a grid reference of 590175, and C, which has a grid reference of 565145. Join up the points to make a triangle ABC.

a A man walks from A to B, from B to C and from C back to A. Work out, to the nearest kilometre, the total length of his walk.

b On his way round he takes certain bearings. Copy and complete this table, showing each bearing to the nearest degree.

c If he walked at a mean speed of 4 km/h, how long did he take to complete his walk?

		Bearing from		
		A	B	C
To	A			
	B			
	C			

4 On graph paper, using a scale of 2 cm to one unit on both axes, mark the Northings from 20 to 24 and the Eastings from 13 to 17. On your map-grid plot points X (140205) and Y (170215).

a Write down the scale of your map-grid in the form 1 : n.

b From X the bearing of a hilltop cairn is 020° and from Y the bearing of the same cairn is 310°. Mark the position of the cairn on your map-grid and write down its grid reference.

c How far, to the nearest kilometre, is the cairn from X?

d Work out the area of the triangle between X, Y and the cairn (i) on the map in cm² (ii) on the land in km².

5 From the point A on the grid-map in Question 1, the bearing of a tower is 149° and from the point B the bearing of the same tower is 073°. What is the grid reference of the tower?

MASTERMINDERS

6 On a map the points A, B, C and D have the following respective grid references: 330180, 355205, 345180 and 355190.

a Find the bearing of D from A.

b A man walks from A to B, from B to C, from C to D and from D back to A.

(i) Find how far the man walks.

(ii) If his walk took three hours, find his mean speed in km/h.

7 Draw a map-grid on graph paper. Using a scale of 2 cm to one unit on both axes, draw a Northing axis from 36 to 41 and an Easting axis from 24 to 31. Plot M (250410) and N (305405).

a A party of walkers from a position P note that the bearing of N is 050° and the bearing of M is 350°. Use these bearings to plot P on your map-grid.

b The party then walks to position Q and notes that the bearing of N is now 016° and the bearing of M is now 301°. Use these bearings to plot Q on your map-grid.

c If the party walked at a mean speed of 4 km/h, find the time it took them to walk from P to Q. Give your answer in hours and minutes.

8 An artillery gun fires three shells from a hidden position. The shells land at (195430), (230445) and (205470). Assuming that the shells all land the same distance from where they were fired, find the grid reference of the firing position.

9 **a** What area of land is represented by a six-figure grid reference? What is this unit of area called?

b How many figures are needed for a grid reference that would define a square metre of land?

__ 12.3 Scale drawing

__ Activity 34

We can find a place on a map if we are given its grid reference. In this Activity you will be introduced to another way of finding a place.

1 On a piece of A4 graph paper, using a scale of 2 cm to one unit on both axes, mark the Northings from 20 to 34 and the Eastings from 60 to 69. On your map-grid plot the point P(640270). (The scale of your map-grid is 1 : 50 000.)

2 Imagine you are at P. Explain where you **could** be if you walked:
a On a bearing of 090° from P.
b A distance of 4.6 km from P.

Explain why you **would** be at 686270 if you walked on a bearing of 090° from P and for a distance of 4.6 km. Plot this point on your map-grid.

3 Copy the table. Use your map-grid to help complete it.

	Distance from P (km)	Bearing from P (°)	Grid reference
a	4.6	090	686270
b	6.1	180	
c	3.2	270	
d	5.0	038	
e	6.0	336	
f	4.9	150	
g	5.5	206	
h	3.7	242	
i	3.0	299	
j	4.4	114	

__ Activity 35

Often we want to define a region on a diagram. In this Activity, we start with a rectangle which represents a field of dimensions 80 m by 40 m. In this field there is a tethered grazing goat.

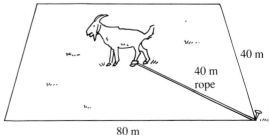

40 m

40 m
rope

80 m

In this diagram the shaded region shows where the goat can graze if it is within 40 m of the corner marked C.

Make separate drawings to show, by shading, where the goat can graze for each of the following conditions.

1 Within 40 m of D.

2 Within 20 m of the fence AB.

3 Nearer to the fence BC than to AD.

4 Within 40 m of the fence AD.

5 Nearer to the corner D than to C.

6 Within 40 m of the mid point of DC.

7 Nearer to the corner A than to C.

8 Within 40 m of the mid point of DC but **also** nearer to AB than to CD.

9 More than 40 m away from B.

10 More than 40 m away from B but **also** nearer to DC than to AB.

A   B

D   C

▬ Exercise 70

1 A party of walkers start from a point A and walk on a bearing of 120° for 8 km to a point B. From B they walk on a bearing of 240° for 6 km to a point C.
Using a scale of 1 cm to 1 km, make an accurate scale drawing of triangle ABC.
Use your drawing to find:
a The distance, in km, of AC.
b The bearing of A from C.

2 A power-boat race is held over a course from A to B to C. There are four possible positions of the buoys, as shown in the table. Using a scale of 1 cm to 1 km, make an accurate scale drawing of each possible course.

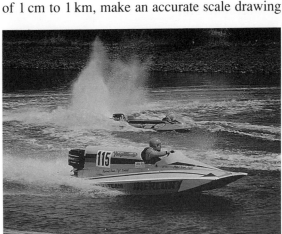

	Distance (km)		Bearing from	
	A to B	B to C	A to B	B to C
a	7	10	215°	070°
b	6.5	5.5	250°	170°
c	8.5	4.5	110°	335°
d	6.5	9	055°	255°

Use your drawings to find, for each course:
(i) The distance, in km, between A and C.
(ii) The bearing of A from C.

3 The diagram represents a straight stretch of coastland running East-West. L is a lifeboat station on the coast 5 km due West of the port of P.
A distress call is received from a ship at S, which is on a bearing of 070° from L and 2 km from P.
Using a scale of 2 cm to 1 km, make a scale drawing showing the positions of L, P and S.
Use your drawing to find the nearest position of S from the coast.

4 A and B are two villages 6 km apart on a straight road running North-South. V is a volcano on a bearing of 140° from A and a bearing of 040° from B.
Using a scale of 2 cm to 1 km, make a scale drawing showing A, B and V.
a If the volcano erupts, anywhere within 3 km is in danger. On your drawing shade the area which would be in danger.
b Use your drawing to find the length of road which is in danger when the volcano erupts. Give your answer to the nearest kilometre.

5 The diagram represents a road running North-South and two crossroads, L and M, 7 km apart. The point G represents an artillery gun which can fire shells up to a distance of 4 km.
The bearing of L from G is 035° and the bearing of M from G is 140°.
Using a scale of 2 cm to 1 km, make a scale drawing of L, M and G.
a Use your drawing to find out what length of the road can be hit by the gun.
b Find the perpendicular distance from the gun to the road, to the nearest 100 m.

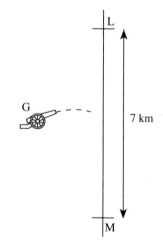

MASTERMINDERS

6 HMS Alligator is 25 nautical miles due West of SS Beatrix at midnight. SS Beatrix is steaming in a South-Easterly direction at a fixed speed. HMS Alligator is steaming on a fixed course at 30 knots. She intercepts SS Beatrix at 02:00. Draw an accurate diagram to show this information and deduce the speed of SS Beatrix. (1 knot = 1 nautical mile per hour)

7 I start at A, run straight for 2 km to B, turn to the left by $x°$, run straight for 1 km to C, turn to the left by $2x°$, run straight for 2 km to D, turn to the left again, run straight for 1 km and am surprised to find myself back at A. I know I have not crossed my tracks anywhere. What was x?

8 The map-grid shows the position of a number of towns in the East Midlands and two BBC TV transmitters at Sandy and Waltham. Each grid square represents $100\,\mathrm{km}^2$.

The strength (T) of a TV signal, at any place, depends on
- Its distance (r) from the transmitter.
- The signal strength (P) transmitted.

The relationship between T, P and r is given by the formula

$$T = \frac{P}{r^2}$$

where T and P are in watts, and r is in metres and greater than or equal to 1.

A TV set operates satisfactorily on a signal strength of 400 microwatts (10^{-6} watts = 1 microwatt.)
The signal strength transmitted from Sandy is 1000 kilowatts and the signal strength from Waltham is 640 kilowatts.

a Use the formula to work out the greatest distance, in km, from each transmitter, for satisfactory reception.

b Copy the map-grid and on it show the area that represents satisfactory reception from both transmitters.

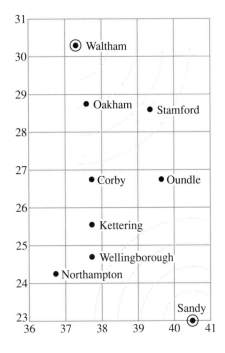

9 How many places on the Earth's surface are there, where if you travel 10 miles South, followed by 10 miles East or West and followed by 10 miles North, you arrive back at your starting point?

__ 12.4 Angle of depression

The angle of depression of a point P, on horizontal ground, from the top of a building, is the angle between the **horizontal** and the line of vision to the point on the ground.

To measure the angle of depression we use a 'clinometer'. This is easily made (see page 161 in Book 1).

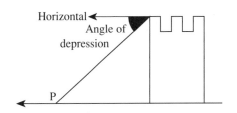

___ *Activity 36*

We want to find the perpendicular height of a hill (A), above a certain point (D), by measuring the angle of depression from A, B and C as shown in the diagram below. You should work in pairs for this Activity.

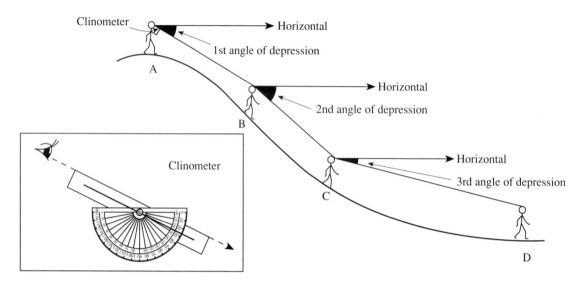

1   One pupil stands at B. The other uses the clinometer to measure the angle of depression from A, to the top of the head of the pupil standing at B. The distance along the ground is then measured from A to B.
The pupil with the clinometer then stands at the point B and the other pupil moves to C, and the second angle of depression is measured. The distance BC is then measured. This process is repeated at C.

2   Use your measurements to draw a diagram, to a suitable scale, of the positions of the four points. Use your drawing to find the perpendicular height of A above D. Explain why you think it is probably necessary to measure three angles of depression.

3   The information in the following table refers to the diagram above. Use this information to make five separate scale drawings showing the points A, B, C and D. Use your drawings to find the perpendicular height of A above D in each case.

	Angle of depression at			Distance (m) between		
	A	B	C	AB	BC	CD
a	20°	15°	12°	8	7	9
b	18°	26°	10°	7.5	18	8
c	15°	22°	30°	25	30	35
d	35°	25°	15°	15	15	15
e	24°	40°	24°	20	20	26

Revision Exercise 12A

1 This map-grid is drawn to a scale of 2 cm to 1 km.
   a What is the grid reference of (i) B   (ii) C?
   b Write the scale of the map-grid in the form 1 : n.
   c Measure the bearing of (i) C from B
      (ii) A from C.
   d Measure the length AC and write down, in km, the distance it represents.
   e Use the map-grid to help work out the area, in km², represented by the triangle ABC.

2 A party of walkers start from a point A and walk on a bearing of 070° for 5 km to a point B. From B they walk on a bearing of 165° for 3 km to a point C. Using a scale of 2 cm to 1 km, make a scale drawing showing the positions of A, B and C. Use your drawing to find:
   a The distance, in km, of A from C.
   b The bearing of A from C.

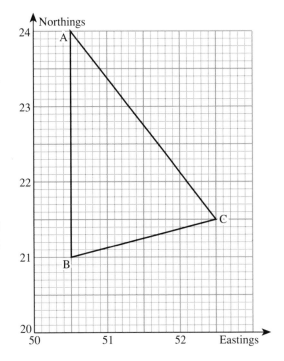

Revision Exercise 12B

1 This map-grid is drawn to a scale of 2 cm to 1 km.
   a What is the grid reference of A?
   b What is the bearing of A from B?
   c What distance, in km, does the line AC represent?
   d Work out the area, in km², represented by the triangle ABC.

2 P and Q are two fishing ports 5 km apart on a straight stretch of coast. The bearing of P from Q is 250°. A yacht in distress is on a bearing of 340° from P and 280° from Q. Using a scale of 2 cm to 1 km, make a scale drawing showing P, Q and the position of the yacht.
   a The lifeboat is stationed on the coast between P and Q and 2 km from Q. On what bearing should it sail?
   b How long will the lifeboat take to reach the yacht, if it can travel at 40 km/h? Give your answer to the nearest minute.

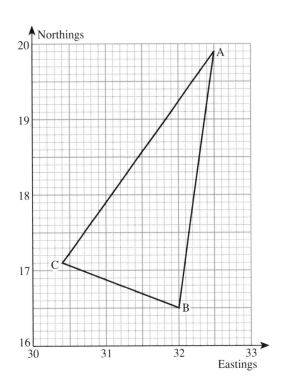

___ Aural Test 4

Twenty questions will be read out to you. You may do any workings on a piece of paper. You will need the following information to answer Questions 11 to 20.

11 and **12**

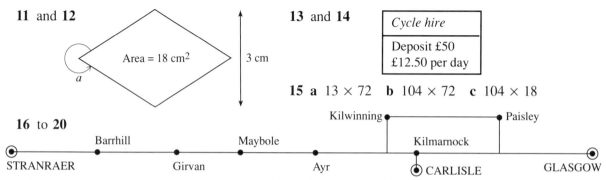

Area = 18 cm²

3 cm

a

13 and **14**

Cycle hire
Deposit £50 £12.50 per day

15 a 13×72 **b** 104×72 **c** 104×18

16 to **20**

Miles	Miles		Timetable		Glasgow – Stranraer									
0	–	Glasgow	d			0800	0857	1000	1127	1435		1635	1800	2157
7.25	–	Paisley	d			0811	0908	1011	1142	1446		1646	1811	2208
26.75	–	Kilwinning	d			0839	0927	1036	1205	1511		1714	1844	2227
–	0	Carlisle	d	0205							1442			
–	91	Kilmarnock	d	0357							1623			
41.5	–	Ayr	a	0419		0909	0952	1105	1224	1544	1644	1746	1917	2248
–	–		d	0428	0600	0715	0915	0953	1110	1225	1548	1646	1751	1919 2253
50.5	–	Maybole	d		0613	0728	0928	1005	1123	1236	1603	1710	1804	1932 2305
62.75	–	Girvan	d	0500	0632	0748	0947	1023	1142	1255	1622	1727	1823	1955 2337
75	–	Barrhill	d			1045		1317					2022	0001
101	166.25	Stranraer	a	0615			1125		1353		1829			0037

Miles	Miles		Timetable		Stranraer – Glasgow									
0	0	Stranraer	d		0730		1100		1300			1830		2200
26	–	Barrhill	d		0805				1335			1905	2035	
38.25	–	Girvan	d	0638	0752	0830	0958	1159	1230	1400	1630	1830	1930	2100 2312
50.5	–	Maybole	d	0656	0810	0846	1020		1252	1418	1648	1848	1948	2118
59.5	–	Ayr	a	0710	0825	0901	1034	1229	1306	1432	1702	1902	2001	2131 2346
–	–		d	0715		0903	1045	1231	1315	1433	1715	1915	2003	2348
–	75.25	Kilmarnock	a					1254						0014
–	166.25	Carlisle	a					1444						0215
74.25	–	Kilwinning	d	0743	0909	0918	1109		1343	1448	1743	1943	2018	2209
93.75	–	Paisley	d	0812	0935	0941	1135		1409	1512	1814	2009	2040	2235
101	–	Glasgow	a	0828	0945	0955	1149		1423	1526	1828	2024	2054	2250

___ Puzzlers

1 Find the maximum distance you could travel, on the above railway network, in twenty-four hours. Give your answer to the nearest mile.

Coursework: Polyhedra constructions

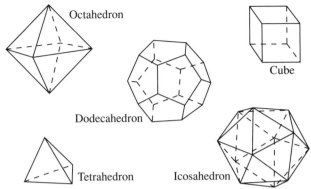

Octahedron
Cube
Dodecahedron
Tetrahedron   Icosahedron

A regular polyhedron is a solid with faces (surfaces) in the shape of a regular polygon. All its edges are therefore the same length.

There are only five regular polyhedra (drawn here) and these were known to the ancient world over 3000 years ago. In this Coursework, you are going to construct all five polyhedra.

1   First, copy and complete the table:

| Polyhedron | Number of | | | Classification | Edge length of model |
	Faces	Vertices	Edges		
Tetrahedron					50 mm
Cube				4^3	30 mm
Octahedron					40 mm
Icosahedron	20				30 mm
Dodecahedron				5^3	See page 200

2   Next, work out and construct the 'net' for the octahedron, tetrahedron, icosahedron and the cube, and make your model from it. You are advised to follow the stages shown below.

NOTE

1 Accurately construct the net on a piece of paper. Use a sharp pencil and do not press too hard.

2 With a compass point, very carefully mark through the vertices of the net onto a piece of thin card. Draw in the fold-lines (the edges). In the correct places, draw each tab 5 mm wide: these tabs are used to glue the model together.

3 With a compass point held at an acute angle to the card, very carefully score along each fold-line. (If this is not done accurately your model will not fit together properly.)

4 Fold along each score-line, so that the score-line is on the **inside** of your model. Use a suitable glue to complete your model.

Each tab should be this shape:

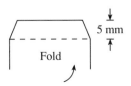

5 mm
Fold

Remember to hold your compass point at an acute angle α to the card when scoring:

compass
α

Coursework: Polyhedra constructions

3 The net for the dodecahedron is shown on the right. Construct this net as follows:

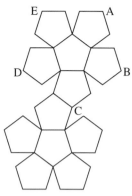

Net for the dodecahedron

a Draw a circle with radius 6 cm. Divide the angle at the centre into five equal angles and hence mark the points A, B, C, D and E as shown.

b The pentagon in the middle is constructed by joining AC, BD, CE, DA and EB.

c Use the pentagon in the middle to help you complete the five outside pentagons.

d To complete the net, you should notice that many other points lie on certain straight lines.

EXTENSION

4 Construct one or more of the following from the nets shown:

Truncated tetrahedron (3 cm edge)

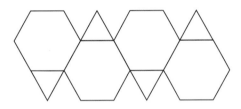

Rhombicuboctahedron (3 cm edge)

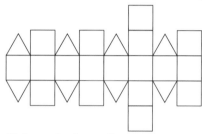

Truncated octahedron (2 cm edge)

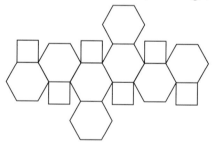

Cuboctahedron (3 cm edge)

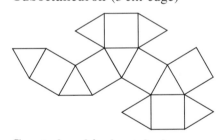

Truncated cube (2 cm edge)

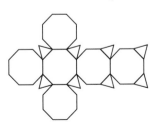

Great rhombicuboctahedron or
Truncated cuboctahedron (1.5 cm edge)

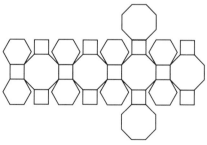

Appendix: Extension work

Circumference of a circle

REMEMBER

Diameter = 2r

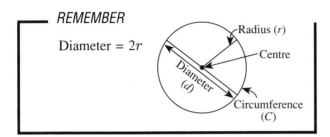

Activity 37

1   Take a circular object such as a screw-on lid and measure its diameter (d) and circumference (C). Work out the ratio of the circumference to the diameter. Repeat this for three other circular objects of different sizes. Copy the table below and enter your results.

Object	Circumference (C)	Diameter (d)	$\frac{C}{d}$

2   What do you notice about the numbers in the last column? If your measurements were accurate, you should have found that $C \div d$ was about 3.14 for all cases. This ratio is always denoted by the Greek letter π.

$$\frac{C}{d} = \pi$$

Therefore $C = \pi d$

REMEMBER

• Circumference of circle = $2\pi r$.

• Use the π button on your calculator.

■ EXAMPLE 1
Find, to 3 SF, the circumference of a wheel of diameter 53.4 cm.

[F] $d = 53.4$ cm, therefore $r = 26.7$ cm.

[E] $C = 2\pi r$

[S] $C = 2\pi 26.7$

[W] $C = 168$ cm to 3 SF

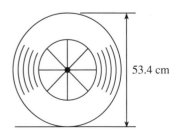

53.4 cm

20 cm

■ EXAMPLE 2

Find the radius of a tin of circumference 20 cm. Give your answer to 3 SF.

[F] $C = 20$ cm

[E] $C = 2\pi r$

[S] $20 = 2\pi r$ (Divide both sides by 2π)

[W] $\frac{20}{2\pi} = r$

$r = 3.18$ cm to 3 SF

___ Exercise 71

Give your answers to 3 SF.

1 Find the circumference of a circle when its radius is:
   a 3 cm   **b** 8 m   **c** 16.7 cm   **d** 34 m   **e** 1.9 mm   **f** 214 cm

2 Find the circumference of a circle when the diameter is:
   a 3 cm   **b** 7 m   **c** 19.8 m   **d** 56 m   **e** 18 mm   **f** 140 cm

3 Find the radius of a circle when its circumference is:
   a 123 cm   **b** 45 m   **c** 98 cm   **d** 16 mm   **e** 12.4 m   **f** 420 mm

4 Which has the longer perimeter, a square of side length 10 cm or a circle of radius 6.37 cm?

5 The handle of a bucket is a semicircle of length 70 cm. Calculate the diameter of the bucket.

6 The wheels of a railway carriage have a diameter of 105 cm. Find:
a The circumference of each wheel.
b The number of revolutions made by each wheel when the carriage travels from London to Leeds, a distance of 297 km.

7 A car is travelling at 100 km/h. The diameter of its wheels is 60 cm.
a Find the circumference of one of its wheels.
b Find the number of revolutions each wheel makes when the car travels 100 km.
c Find the number of revolutions each wheel makes in 1 hour.
d Find the number of revolutions each wheel makes per second.

8 Assume the Earth moves in a circular orbit around the Sun once every $365\frac{1}{4}$ days. If the distance from the Earth to the Sun is 90 million miles, find the speed of the Earth around the Sun.

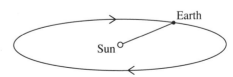

9 Assume the planet Uranus moves in a circular orbit around the Sun once every 84 years. If the distance from Uranus to the Sun is 1.8 billion miles, find its speed around the Sun.

10 The Earth spins about its North to South axis once every 24 hours. London and Singapore are 3970 km and 6380 km respectively from this axis.

  a Find the speed at which a pupil moves about the axis (i) in London   (ii) in Singapore.

  b How far will each pupil travel during a 45-minute Maths lesson?

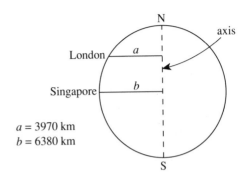

$a = 3970$ km
$b = 6380$ km

Area of a circle

Activity 38

This Activity demonstrates the following equation:

> **NOTE**
>
> Area of a circle = πr^2

1 On a piece of card draw a circle of radius 3.5 cm. Draw 18 diameters such that the angle between any adjacent pair is 10°. Carefully cut out the 36 areas (called 'sectors').

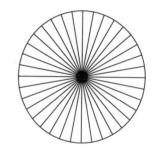

2 On a separate piece of paper, draw a rectangle whose length is equal to one half of the circumference of the circle and whose width is equal to the radius of the circle. Carefully stick all your sectors onto the rectangle as shown. (You will need to cut one sector in half.)

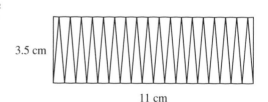

3.5 cm

11 cm

This shows that the area of the circle and rectangle are equal.

We can also show this by calculation:

  Area of the circle (from equation above) $= \pi 3.5^2 = 38.48$ cm^2

  Area of the rectangle (from part 2) $= \frac{1}{2} \times$ Circumference of the circle $\times$ Radius of the circle

    (Circumference of the circle $= 2\pi 3.5 = 21.99$ cm)

  Therefore area of the rectangle $= \frac{1}{2} \times 21.99 \times 3.5 = 38.48$ cm^2

■ *EXAMPLE 1*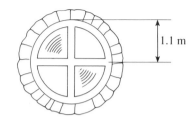

Find the area of a circular window of radius 1.1 m.

[F] $r = 1.1\,\text{m}$

[E] $A = \pi r^2$

[S] $A = \pi 1.1^2$

[W] $A = 3.80\,\text{m}^2$ to 3 SF

■ *EXAMPLE 2*

Find the radius of a circular pond of area $20\,\text{m}^2$.

$A = 20\,\text{m}^2$

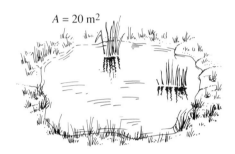

[F] $A = 20\,\text{m}^2$

[E] $A = \pi r^2$

[S] $20 = \pi r^2$ (Divide both sides by π)

[W] $\frac{20}{\pi} = r^2$ (Square root both sides)

$$\sqrt{\frac{20}{\pi}} = r$$

$$r = 2.52\,\text{m} \text{ to 3 SF}$$

___ Exercise 72

Give your answers to 3 SF.

1   Find the area of a circle when its radius is:
      a 4 cm   **b** 6.9 cm   **c** 12 mm   **d** 7.2 m   **e** 30 m   **f** 47.3 mm

2   Find the radius of a circle when its area is:
      a $8.4\,\text{cm}^2$ **b** $3\,\text{cm}^2$ **c** $46\,\text{mm}^2$ **d** $8\,\text{m}^2$ **e** $46\,\text{m}^2$ **f** $31\,\text{km}^2$

3   Find the diameter of a circle when its area is:
      a $5\,\text{cm}^2$ **b** $8\,\text{cm}^2$ **c** $5.9\,\text{mm}^2$ **d** $9\,\text{m}^2$ **e** $12.9\,\text{m}^2$ **f** $130\,\text{km}^2$

4   A farmer irrigates part of a field with a high pressure hose which sprays water over a circular area of radius 75 m. Find the area irrigated in hectares. (1 hectare = 10 000 m²)

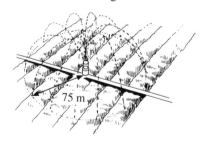

75 m

5   Which has the greater area, a square of side length 10 cm or a circle of radius 5.8 cm?

6 🔳 Find the area of the shapes.

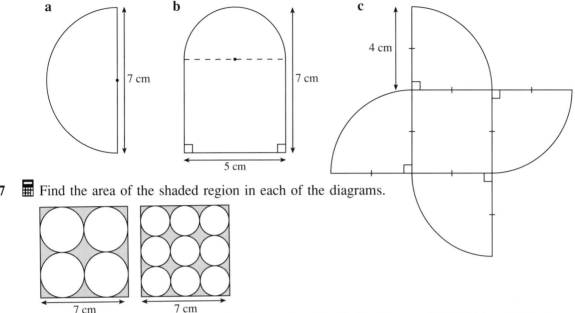

7 🔳 Find the area of the shaded region in each of the diagrams.

Use your answers to work out the shaded region of a similar figure with 100 identical circles.

Pythagoras' theorem

Activity 39 🔳

1 Use your ruler to draw the grid shown in Figure 1. Onto your grid draw the numbered areas.

Use your drawing as a template to copy Figure 1 onto a piece of card. Cut out the six pieces and number them.

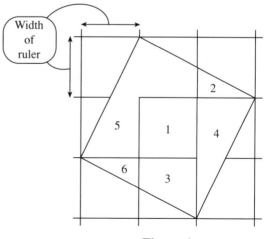

Figure 1

(*Continued*)

205

2   Use your pieces to help make a copy of
Figure 2.

Look at the three different-size squares.
What do you notice about the area of the
two smaller squares relative to the area of the
largest?

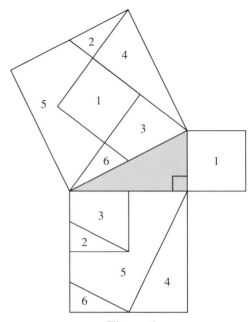

Figure 2

3   If the width of your ruler is x cm, write down
in terms of x the area of each of the six
pieces. Use your answers to write down the
area of the two largest squares in terms of x.
What do you notice?

The result of your experiment shows that, in
a right-angled triangle, the following is true:

NOTE

Pythagoras' theorem:
$$c^2 = a^2 + b^2$$

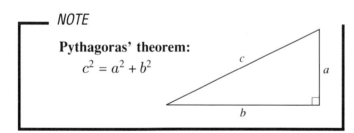

This fact was first discovered by the Egyptians over 3000 years ago, but it was not until 500
years later that the Greek mathematician Pythagoras actually proved this remarkable fact.

■*EXAMPLE 1*

Find the value of x to 3 SF:

a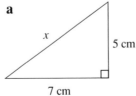

b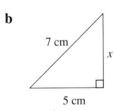

a   [F]   See diagram

[E] and [S] $x^2 = 7^2 + 5^2$ (Square root both sides)

[W] $x = \sqrt{7^2 + 5^2}$

$x = 8.60$ cm to 3 SF

b [F]   See diagram (previous page)

[E] and [S] $7^2 = x^2 + 5^2$ (Subtract 5^2 from both sides)

[W] $7^2 - 5^2 = x^2$ (Square root both sides)

$$\sqrt{7^2 - 5^2} = x$$

$$x = 4.90 \text{ cm to 3 SF}$$

■ EXAMPLE 2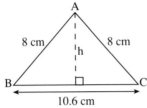

Find the perpendicular height of A above BC in the isosceles triangle ABC.

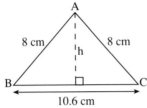

[F]   See diagram (the perpendicular from A bisects the base BC)

[E] and [S] $8^2 = h^2 + 5.3^2$

[W] $\sqrt{8^2 - 5.3^2} = h$

$$h = 5.99 \text{ cm to 3 SF}$$

── Exercise 73

Give all your answers to 3 SF.

1   Find the value of x.

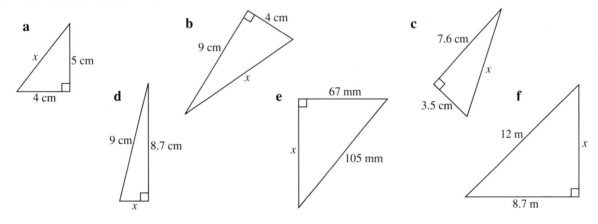

2   Find the length of a diagonal of a rectangle with sides of 9.3 m and 17.3 m.

3   The diagonals of a rhombus are 53 cm and 37 cm. Find its perimeter.

4 ▦ Triangle ABC is isosceles. Copy and complete the table below. Show your working for each part. All lengths are in centimetres.

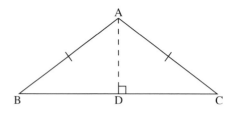

	AD	BD	AB	BC	Area ABC
a	3	4			
b	6		10		
c		7	9		
d	5			9.8	
e			8	15	
f				20	45 cm²
g	8				18 cm²

5 ▦ The diagram shows the side of a 'lean-to' shed. Find:
a The height of the door AB.
b The area of the side of the shed.

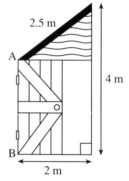

6 ▦ Calculate the area of a square whose diagonals are each 10 cm long.

7 ▦ A television tower stands on level ground and is supported by a wire from the top which is fixed to the ground 220 m from the base of the tower. If the wire is 500 m long, calculate the height of the tower.

▬ Prisms

Any solid with parallel sides has a constant cross-section. The volume of such a solid is the product of the cross-sectional area and the length (or height). These solids are called **prisms**.

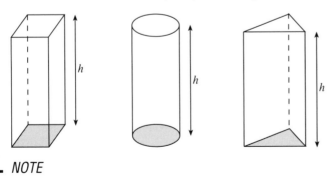

─ *NOTE*

Volume of prism = Cross-sectional area × Height

___ *Activity 40*

Take a rectangular piece of
paper and make it into a
hollow cylinder, like this:

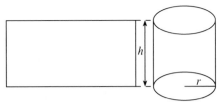

Use your paper cylinder to explain why a cylinder has the following properties:

- Volume $V = \pi r^2 \times h$
- Curved surface area $A = 2\pi rh$

___ Exercise 74

Give your answers to 3 SF.

Questions 1 to 3 refer to the cylinder drawn in Activity 40.

1 The height (h) of a cylinder is 12 cm. Find its volume if its radius (r) is:
   a 10 cm   **b** 25 cm   **c** 5.6 cm   **d** 3.5 cm

2 The diameter of a cylinder is 6 cm. Find the curved surface area if its height (h) is:
   a 4 cm   **b** 12 cm   **c** 7.9 cm   **d** 67 cm

3 Copy the table below and complete it when the radius of a cylinder is 5 cm.

	Height (cm)	Volume (cm³)	Curved surface area (cm²)
a	12		
b	24		
c		11	
d		22	
e			45
f			90

4 Twelve cans of baked beans are tightly packed
into a box as shown. If each tin has a volume of
508 cm³ and a height of 11.5 cm, find the internal
dimensions of the box.

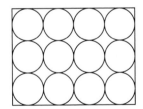

5 The largest salami ever made was 5.74 m long, had a circumference of 71 cm and a mass of
207.2 kg. Find the mass in grams per cm³. What is this a measure of?

6 **Investigate**, by calculation, the length of toothpaste which can be squeezed from a tube of
toothpaste.

Multiple Choice Test 1

NOTE

For Chapters 1 to 3. (Ask your teacher if you should do the extension.)
Calculators are **not** allowed. Do **not** write on this page. Show all your working clearly.
Write down the **letter** which you think corresponds to the correct answer.

1 The number 0.046 506 written to 3 significant figures is:

   a 0.047   **b** 0.05   **c** 0.0466   **d** 0.0465   **e** 0.04651

2 The approximate value of $\dfrac{684 \times 0.073}{46.2}$ is:

   a 500   **b** 100   **c** 50   **d** 1   **e** 10

3 If £3.50 is increased by 30% the result is:

   a £10.50   **b** £7   **c** £1.05   **d** £4.55   **e** None of these

4 The value of $x - y(y - x)$ when $x = 3$ and $y = 2$ is:

   a -1 **b** 1   **c** -9 **d** -5 **e** None of these

5 The value of x in $36 = 2x + 3$ is:

   a 66   **b** 21   **c** 15   **d** $18\frac{1}{2}$ **e** $16\frac{1}{2}$

6 The number of pence in £$(10 + y)$ is:

   a $1000 + y$ **b** $100 + 10y$ **c** $110 + y$ **d** $100 + y$ **e** $1000 + 100y$

7 Simplify $2x - 2(x + 2) + 2(x - 2)$.

   a $2x - 8$ **b** $6x - 8$ **c** $2x - 6$ **d** $6x$ **e** $2x + 8$

8 The actual length of the USS New Jersey is 270 m (the longest warship in the world). The scale of this photograph is:

   a 1 : 300   **b** 2000 : 1   **c** 1 : 20   **d** 1 : 2000   **e** 1 : 200

9 Change 3080 cm^2 to m^2.

   a 30.8 m^2 **b** 3.08 m^2 **c** 308 000 m^2 **d** 0.308 m^2 **e** 308 m^2

10 Nine CDs cost £58.50. How much do eight cost?

   a £66   **b** £52   **c** £53.50   **d** £54.50   **e** None of these

11 The scale of a map is 1 : 100 000. What is the distance between two places on the map if they are 5 km apart on the land?

   a 0.5 mm   **b** 5 cm   **c** 5 mm   **d** 50 cm   **e** 500 m

12 The nth term in the sequence -1, 1, 3, 5, ... is:

   a $2n + 3$ **b** $3n - 2$ **c** $3n + 2$ **d** $2n - 3$ **e** None of these

13 The value of x in the equation $3 + \frac{3}{x} = 33$ is:

   a 0.1   **b** 12   **c** 11   **d** $\frac{3}{11}$ **e** None of these

14 When minus 4 is subtracted from 10 the result is:

   a 6   **b** -6 **c** 14   **d** -14 **e** None of these

15 Gill has £9.80 pocket money. She spends one half on presents, one quarter on perfume and one fifth on a pen. The amount she has left is:

   a 54p   **b** 49p   **c** 98p   **d** 94p   **e** None of these

EXTENSION

16 Clive's age is x years and his mother is five times as old. What will be their **combined** age in y years time?

   a $6x + y$ years   **b** $6x + 2y$ years   **c** $6x + 5y$ years   **d** $6xy$ years   **e** $x + 2y$ years

17 1 kg $\approx$ 2.2 pounds. Which of the following is nearest to 12 pounds?

   a 1 kg   **b** 3 kg   **c** 5 kg   **d** 7 kg   **e** 9 kg

18 The number of minutes in forty years is approximately:

   a 13 million   **b** 31 million   **c** 21 million   **d** 130 million   **e** 0.5 million

19 The density of air is 1.2 kg/m^3. The mass of air in a room of dimensions 6 m $\times$ 5 m $\times$ 2 m is:

   a 720 kg   **b** 7.2 g   **c** 72 kg   **d** 7.2 kg   **e** 720 g

20 A bottle has a mass of 280 g when empty. When it is full of water, the total mass is 540 g. When half full of water, the total mass is:

   a 270 g   **b** 130 g   **c** 410 g   **d** 140 g   **e** 260 g

Multiple Choice Test 2

NOTE

For Chapters 4 to 6. (Ask your teacher if you should do the extension.)
Calculators are **not** allowed. Do **not** write on this page. Show all your working clearly.
Write down the **letter** which you think corresponds to the correct answer.

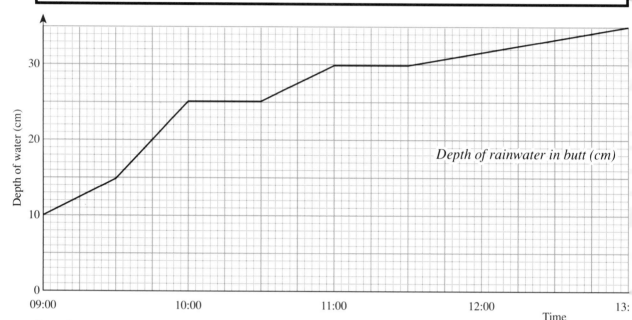

Depth of rainwater in butt (cm)

Questions 1 to 5 refer to the graph above, which shows the depth of water in a
rainwater butt. The butt has parallel sides and a rectangular base of 60 cm by 20 cm.

1 The distance between adjacent lines on the graph paper is 2 mm. Which scale is correct?
  a 2 cm to 50 mm **b** 2 cm to 20 min **c** 2 cm to 15 min **d** 1 cm to 100 mm **e** 1 cm to 15 min

2 What is the depth of water at 10:45?
  a 25 cm   **b** 30 cm   **c** 27.5 cm   **d** 26 cm   **e** 28 cm

3 Between which times did the most rain fall?
  a 09:00 to 09:30 **b** 10:00 to 11:30 **c** 10:30 to 11:30 **d** 09:30 to 10:00 **e** 11:30 to 13:00

4 What is the mean increase in depth per hour between 09:00 and 11:00?
  a 30 cm   **b** 10 cm   **c** 7.5 cm   **d** 2.5 cm   **e** 15 cm

5 What would you expect the increase in the volume of water in the tank to be between 09:00 and
13:00?
  a 42 000 cm^3 **b** 4.2 m^3 **c** 30 000 cm^3 **d** 3 m^3 **e** 0.042 m^3

6 A rectangular carpet is $4y$ metres long and $3x$ metres wide. Its area in m^2 is:
  a $12xy^2$ **b** $12x^2y$ **c** $12xy$ **d** $4xy$ **e** $12x^2y^2$

7 The perimeter of the carpet in Question 6, in metres, is:
  a $4y + 3x$ **b** $3x + 4y$ **c** $2(4y + 3x)$ **d** $12xy$ **e** None of these

8 The angle between the two hands of a clock at 7 pm is:
   a 150°   **b** 25°   **c** 120°   **d** 135°   **e** 180°

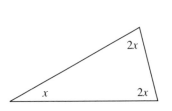

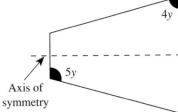

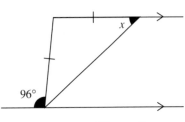

Figure 1   **Figure 2**   **Figure 3**

9 In Figure 1 the value of x is:
   a 40°   **b** 36°   **c** 35°   **d** 32°   **e** 45°

10 In Figure 2 the value of y is:
   a 20°   **b** 24°   **c** 18°   **d** 15°   **e** 10°

11 In Figure 3 the value of x is:
   a 52°   **b** 84°   **c** 96°   **d** 42°   **e** None of these

12 Simplified, $(3y)^2 \times y$ equals:
   a $3y^2$ **b** $9y^2$ **c** $9y^3$ **d** $3y^2$ **e** $9y$

13 Simplified, $(3y)^2 \div y$ equals:
   a $9y^3$ **b** $9y$ **c** $9y^2$ **d** $3y$ **e** $3y^2$

14 When $a = 3$ and $b = -1$, the value of $a^2 - b^2$ is:
   a 4   **b** -10 **c** 10   **d** -8 **e** 8

15 Which of the following has rotational symmetry order 2 but no line symmetry?
   a Rectangle   **b** Square   **c** Rhombus   **d** Parallelogram   **e** Isosceles trapezium

EXTENSION

16 Which one of the following angles can be the interior angle of a regular polygon?
   a 152°   **b** 144°   **c** 148°   **d** 138°   **e** 153°

17 When $a = 3$, $b = -2$ and $c = -1$, the value of $(ab)^2 - c$ is:
   a 35   **b** -37 **c** 37   **d** -35 **e** None of these

18 Factorize completely the expression $4xy^2 - 12x^2y$:
   a $4x(y^2 - 3xy)$ **b** $4y(xy - 3x^2)$ **c** $4xy(y - 3x)$ **d** $xy(y - 3xy)$ **e** $xy(4y - 12x)$

19 The carpet in Question 6 costs £c. The cost, in pounds per square metre, is:
   a $\frac{c}{12xy}$ **b** $\frac{c}{3x+4y}$ **c** $c(3x + 4y)$ **d** $\frac{c}{12xy^2}$ **e** $\frac{c}{2(4y+3y)}$

20 From the graph on the previous page, the mass of water in the tank at 10:15 is about:
   a 30 tonnes   **b** 30 kg   **c** 300 kg   **d** 3 tonnes   **e** 0.3 tonne

213

Multiple Choice Test 3

> **NOTE**
>
> For Chapters 7 to 9. (Ask your teacher if you should do the extension.)
> Calculators are **not** allowed. Do **not** write on this page. Show all your working clearly.
> Write down the **letter** which you think corresponds to the correct answer.

1 How many times larger or smaller is 10^8 than 10^{10}?
  a Twice as small **b** Twice as large **c** 10 times smaller **d** 100 times smaller **e** 100 times larg

2 Which is the odd one out?
  a 10^{-2} **b** $\frac{1}{10}$ **c** 0.01   **d** $\frac{1}{10^2}$ **e** $\frac{1}{100}$

3 When 1200 is increased by 5%, the result is:
  a 1250   **b** 1260   **c** 1205   **d** 60   **e** 1140

4 In a tin of biscuits, 66 are chocolate and 84 are plain. What percentage are chocolate?
  a 26%   **b** 21%   **c** 78%   **d** 56%   **e** 44%

5 30 906 written in standard form correct to 3 SF is:
  a 3.09×10^2 **b** 3.091×10^3 **c** 3.091×10^4 **d** 30.9×10^4 **e** 3.09×10^4

6 There are 240 pupils at Rosehill School. A pie chart is drawn to illustrate how they travel to school. 60 pupils walk to school. 80 travel by bus. 70 travel by car. The angle to represent those who travel by other means is:
  a 20°   **b** 30°   **c** 40°
  d 45°   **e** 60°

7 Figure 1 illustrates sports chosen by 180 pupils at Boxhill School. The number who chose athletics is:
  a 60   **b** 90   **c** 30
  d 15   **e** 45

8 The probability of selecting at random a pupil from Boxhill School who chose to play tennis is:
  a $\frac{1}{2}$ **b** $\frac{1}{3}$ **c** $\frac{2}{3}$
  d $\frac{1}{6}$ **e** $\frac{5}{6}$

Figure 1 (For Questions 7 and 8)

9 A card is randomly selected from an ordinary pack of 52 cards. The probability that it is a red queen is:
  a $\frac{1}{13}$ **b** $\frac{2}{13}$ **c** $\frac{1}{12}$ **d** $\frac{1}{2}$ **e** $\frac{1}{26}$

10 Figure 2 shows Penny's counter on a 'Snakes and Ladders' board. On her next throw, with an ordinary die, the probability that she will go down a snake is:
  a $\frac{1}{6}$ **b** $\frac{1}{5}$ **c** $\frac{1}{4}$ **d** $\frac{1}{3}$ **e** $\frac{5}{6}$

Figure 2

214

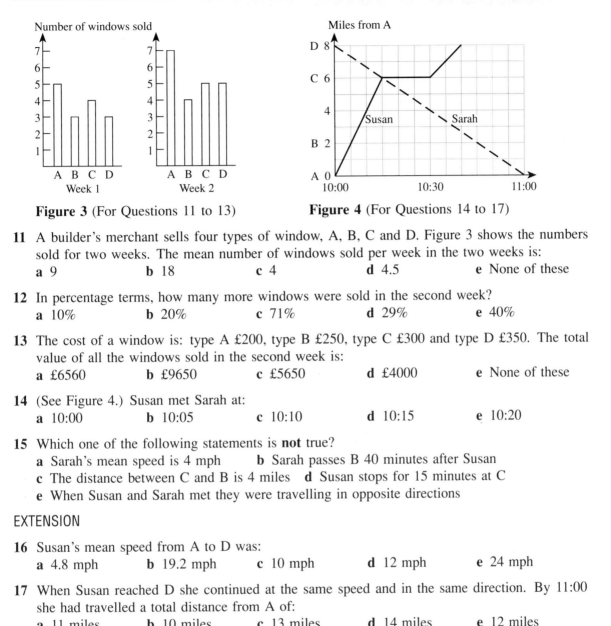

Figure 3 (For Questions 11 to 13)   **Figure 4** (For Questions 14 to 17)

11 A builder's merchant sells four types of window, A, B, C and D. Figure 3 shows the numbers sold for two weeks. The mean number of windows sold per week in the two weeks is:
  a 9   **b** 18   **c** 4   **d** 4.5   **e** None of these

12 In percentage terms, how many more windows were sold in the second week?
  a 10%   **b** 20%   **c** 71%   **d** 29%   **e** 40%

13 The cost of a window is: type A £200, type B £250, type C £300 and type D £350. The total value of all the windows sold in the second week is:
  a £6560   **b** £9650   **c** £5650   **d** £4000   **e** None of these

14 (See Figure 4.) Susan met Sarah at:
  a 10:00   **b** 10:05   **c** 10:10   **d** 10:15   **e** 10:20

15 Which one of the following statements is **not** true?
  a Sarah's mean speed is 4 mph   **b** Sarah passes B 40 minutes after Susan
  c The distance between C and B is 4 miles   **d** Susan stops for 15 minutes at C
  e When Susan and Sarah met they were travelling in opposite directions

EXTENSION

16 Susan's mean speed from A to D was:
  a 4.8 mph   **b** 19.2 mph   **c** 10 mph   **d** 12 mph   **e** 24 mph

17 When Susan reached D she continued at the same speed and in the same direction. By 11:00 she had travelled a total distance from A of:
  a 11 miles   **b** 10 miles   **c** 13 miles   **d** 14 miles   **e** 12 miles

18 How many times larger or smaller is 10^{-3} than 10^{-5}?
  a Twice as small **b** Twice as large **c** 10 times smaller
  d 100 times smaller   **e** 100 times larger

19 A metre is increased by 10 mm. The percentage increase is:
  a 1%   **b** 0.1%   **c** 10%   **d** 0.01%   **e** 101%

20 The numbers in a school decrease from 950 to 874. This is a decrease of:
  a 92%   **b** 5%   **c** 4%   **d** 7%   **e** 8%

Multiple Choice Test 4

NOTE

For Chapters 10 to 12. (Ask your teacher if you should do the extension.)
Calculators are **not** allowed. Do **not** write on this page. Show all your working clearly.
Write down the **letter** which you think corresponds to the correct answer.

1 B is mapped onto D by:

a A reflection in $y = 0$

b A translation of $\begin{pmatrix} 2 \\ 0 \end{pmatrix}$

c A reflection in $y = 1$

d A reflection in $x = 0$

e A translation of $\begin{pmatrix} -2 \\ 0 \end{pmatrix}$

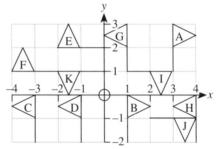

Figure 1 (for questions 1 to 6)

2 A translation of $\begin{pmatrix} 2 \\ 1 \end{pmatrix}$ maps:

a B onto A   b E onto F   c J onto I   d I onto J   e F onto E

3 Which one of the following is **not** true?

a F can be rotated onto A   b A can be rotated onto J

c C can be rotated onto F   d I can be rotated onto E

e G can be rotated onto K

4 K is rotated onto D. The centre of rotation is:

a $(-3, 1)$ b $(-2, -1)$ c $(-2, 1)$ d $(-2, 0)$ e $(-1, 0)$

5 Which one of the following is true?

a G is mapped onto A by reflection in $y = 2$ b C is mapped onto H by translation $\begin{pmatrix} 0 \\ 7 \end{pmatrix}$

c C is mapped onto D by reflection in $x = -2$ d E is mapped onto K by reflection in $y = 1.5$

e J is mapped onto B by rotation 90° clockwise about $(2, -2)$

6 Which one of the following reflections takes place in the line $y = x$?

a K onto E   b G onto I   c A onto G   d J onto G   e B onto D

7 The inequality which is represented by the number line is:

a $x > 0$ and $x < 3$ b $x \leqslant 0$ and $x > 3$

c $x \geqslant 0$ and $x < 3$ d $x < 0$ and $x \geqslant 3$ e $x > 0$ and $x \leqslant 3$

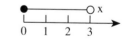

8 The area of a rhombus with diagonals of 18 cm and 6 cm is:

a $27 \, \text{cm}^2$ b $54 \, \text{cm}^2$ c $72 \, \text{cm}^2$ d $108 \, \text{cm}^2$ e $216 \, \text{cm}^2$

9 The bearing of Hilltop S from Hilltop T is 305°. The bearing of Hilltop T from Hilltop S is:

a 035°   b 125°   c 145°   d 205°   e 235°

10 A car travels for 40 km at 20 km/h and then for 20 minutes at 90 km/h. Its mean speed is:

a 55 km/h   b 45 km/h   c 60 km/h   d 30 km/h   e None of these

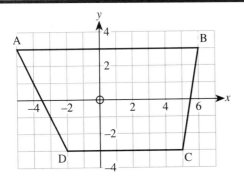

Figure 3 (For Questions 11 and 12)

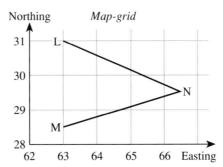

Figure 4 (For Questions 13 to 16)

11 Which of the following is true?
   a ABCD has no rotational symmetry order 2   **b** AB is parallel to $x = 0$
   c ABCD is an isosceles trapezium   **d** The co-ordinate of D is $(-3, -2)$
   e ABCD has an axis of symmetry

12 The area of ABCD is:
   a 51 square units **b** 21 square units **c** 30 square units **d** 57 square units **e** 54 square units

13 (See Figure 4.) The grid reference of N is:
   a 6629   **b** 295665   **c** 620285   **d** 665305   **e** 665295

14 If the distance between adjacent Eastings (and Northings) is 2 cm, the scale of the map-grid is
   1 : 50 000. On this scale the approximate area represented by the triangle LMN is:
   a 0.4 km^2 **b** 2 km^2 **c** 4 km^2 **d** 8 km^2 **e** 40 km^2

15 If the distance between adjacent Eastings (and Northings) is 4 cm, the scale of the map-grid is:
   a 1 : 100 000   **b** 1 : 2500   **c** 1 : 50 000   **d** 1 : 5000   **e** 1 : 25 000

EXTENSION

16 The bearing of M from N nearly equals:
   a 015°   **b** 255°   **c** 055°   **d** 285°   **e** 105°

17 At 10.00 am a woman starts walking at 6 km/h to a station 9 km away. She waits there for a
   quarter of an hour before returning by bicycle at 18 km/h. She arrives back at:
   a 12.45 pm   **b** 12.00 noon   **c** 11.45 am   **d** 12.15 pm   **e** None of these

18 In the inequality $3x < 5x + 4$, x is:
   a < -2 **b** > 2 **c** > -2 **d** $< -\frac{1}{2}$ **e** $> -\frac{1}{2}$

19 There are 20 questions in a test. 5 marks are given for each correct answer. 1 mark is deducted
   for each unanswered or incorrect answer. Sarah gets n questions correct. Her total mark, in
   terms of n, is:
   a $4n - 20$ **b** $6n - 20$ **c** $100 - 20n$ **d** $5n - 20$ **e** $100 - 5n$

20 Which pair of co-ordinates lie on the line $y = -x$?
   a $(8, 8), (8, -8)$ **b** $(8, 8), (-8, -8)$ **c** $(-8, 8), (8, -8)$
   d $(8, -8), (-8, -8)$ **e** $(-8, 8), (8, 8)$

ACKNOWLEDGEMENTS

The author would like to thank his wife for her tireless support and encouragement from the inception of this work, and his father for providing so many ideas for the Puzzlers; Douglas Butler and Keith Oakley for offering invaluable advice during the development of the material; Nick Owens, John Hunt and Walter Holmstrom for providing ideas for questions. He is also indebted to countless pupils for providing so much inspiration over the years, without which this series of books would never have got off the ground; and last, but by no means least, to the team from Longman, Nina Konrad, Sophie Clark and Hendrina Ellis, who launched this edition.

Photographs

Barnaby's Picture Library 85, 106, 119, 167; The Duke of Edinburgh's Award photo: Alan Russell 191; Frank Lane Picture Agency 29, 134 bottom right and left, 168; Grand Metropolitan 93; Robert Harding Picture Library 56, 58, 59, 193; Holt Studios International 84; N.H.P.A. 113, 134 top right and left, 134 centre right and left; Panos Pictures 120; Shell UK 6; Topham Picture Source 81; USS Navy 210; John Walmsley 127.

Thomas Thomas (1790) *Reading, poetry, writing and arithmetic* (collection V. Hony) 46.

Judith Sharpe (garden designer) sketch 51.